Workbook

Frencn

False beginners

Estelle Demontrond-Box

About this book

With 200 exercises divided into 20 chapters, this book will give you the opportunity to carry out a systematic and progressive revision of the French grammar basics. From French pronunciation and alphabet to the Past Tense.

This easy-to-use workbook has been designed specifically for false beginners in French. It includes 200 fun-filled exercises (with answers) which follow a logical progression. You will be able to self-assess your level at the end of each chapter. Every aspect of the language has been covered, including grammar, spelling, vocabulary, syntax, pronunciation and accentuation.

Finally, this book will allow you to carry out a self-assessment: you will be able to fill in your icon's expression after each exercise (☺ for mostly correct, ☺ for approximately half correct and ☹ for less than half). You will then be able to carry forward the number of icons for all of these exercises at the end of each chapter and to add it all up by carrying out the end of chapter icons forward to the table provided for that purpose at the end of the book.

Contents

Alphabet and Pronunciation

The alphabet

The French alphabet is the same as the English one, although the letters are pronounced differently:

A	ah	G	jzay	M	em	S	es	Y	eegrek
B	bay	H	ash	N	en	T	tay	Z	zed
C	say	I	ee	O	oh	U	ew		
D	day	J	jzee	P	pay	V	vay		
E	uh	K	kah	Q	kew	W	doobluh vay		
F	ef	L	el	R	er	X	eeks		

1 Spell the following words aloud in French.

B-O-N-J-O-U-R
(hello)

C-H-A-I-S-E
(chair)

M-A-M-A-N
(mummy)

H-E-U-R-E-U-X
(happy, masc)

Q-U-E-S-T-I-O-N

F-L-E-U-R
(flower)

R-A-V-I-E
(pleased, fem)

V-R-A-I
(true, masc)

G-E-N-T-I-L-L-E
(kind, fem)

W-A-G-O-N

P-A-P-Y
(granddad)

Z-O-O

Accents, diaeresis and cedilla

The French language also uses **accents, diaeresis and cedilla**:

- The acute accent or **l'accent aigu [é]** is used on the letter **[e]** to modify its sound to *eh*.
- The grave accent or **l'accent grave [è]** is mainly used on the letter **[e]** to modify its sound to *ay* but also on **[a]** or **[u]** to distinguish words which otherwise look alike.
- The circumflex accent or **l'accent circonflexe** is used on letters **[a]**, **[e]**, **[i]**, **[o]** and **[u]**.
- The diaeresis or **le tréma** is used to indicate that a vowel must be pronounced independently from others as in **Noël** (*no-ehl*).
- Finally, the cedilla or **la cédille** is used on the letter **[c]** to make the sound **[s]** before the letters **[a]**, **[o]** or **[u]** as in **ça**.

2 Using a dictionary, place the correct accents, diaeresis (*tréma*) or cedilla on the following words and write their meaning as in the example.

Eg.: Frere → frère = brother

a. Une mere → _ _ _ _ = _ _ _ _ _ _ _

b. Peut-etre → _ _ _ _ _ _ _ _ _ _ = _ _ _ _ _

c. Noel → _ _ _ _ = _ _ _ _ _ _ _ _ _ _

d. Une lecon → _ _ _ _ _ _ = _ _ _ _ _ _ _

e. Le present → _ _ _ _ _ _ _ _ = _ _ _ _ _ _ _ _

f. Tot → _ _ _ = _ _ _ _ _

g. Un garcon → _ _ _ _ _ _ _ = _ _ _

h. Le passe → _ _ _ _ _ _ = _ _ _ _

3 Underline the right answer in the following sentences.

a. Mon **pere / pêre / pére / père** est au travail.

b. Il me tarde d'être à **Noêl / Noél / Noël / Noèl** !

c. Pourriez-vous me donner des **glassons / glasons / glacons / glaçons** s'il vous plaît ?

d. Oublie le **passe / passè / passé / passê**. Pense au futur !

e. Elles portent la **meme / mème / méme / même** robe !

SAMEDI
DÉCEMBRE
25

Silent letters

Unfortunately, French is rarely pronounced as it is written. Certain letters are not pronounced at all!

- This often occurs at the end of words, such as
  – with **final consonants: Salut** _Hi_;
  – and silent **[e]: Femme** _Woman_.

- It also occurs with the letter **[h]** which is always silent: **Homme** _Man_.

4 Read the following words aloud (mind the silent letters) and write the English translation below each word.

froid	porc	trois	vous	abricot
....	....	....	....	....
chez	mot	chat	salut	outil
....	....	....	....	....
estomac	beaucoup	trop	nerf	deux
....	....	....	....	....

5 Place the following words in the adequate column according to whether they end up with a silent letter or not.

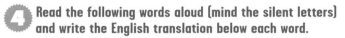

TURC   POULE   HIVER   FOUR   LOURD   OURS   FROID   ŒUF

Silent Letter	Pronounced Letter

Nasal vowels, the [u] and [r] sounds

- **The nasal vowels** are vowels sounds that occur with syllables ending with **[m]** or **[n]** (as in **tante** *aunt*, **oncle** *uncle*). Though these letters are silent, they make the preceding vowel sounds "nasal". These sounds do not exist in English but you can try and approximate them by pronouncing the sound **[–ng]** (as in *song*) and stopping before the **–g** sound.

- **The French U:** this is not like the English **[oo]** sound but closer to the **[ew]** sound. To pronounce it, purse your lips tightly with the tongue towards the front of the mouth, its tip resting against the lower teeth.

- **The French RRRRRRRRRRRRRR!:** The pet hate of most English-speaking French language learners! But it does not have to be! It is simply a guttural sound close to the Spanish **[j]** jota or to the Scottish **[ch]** as in Loch Ness. To pronounce it, try and place the base of your tongue at the back of your throat and then place the tip of your tongue behind the lower teeth as if you were coughing up a hairball!

6 Try and practice the following nasal vowels, and [u] and [r] sounds by reading the following sentences aloud.

a. Tu es sûr que la poule est sur le mur ?

b. Où est ton chien ? Dessus ou dessous le banc ?

c. As-tu entendu ? Sa sœur a eu un garçon !

d. J'ai perdu le numéro de téléphone de sa tante.

Liaison

The letters **s, x, z, t, d, n,** and **m** which are normally silent at the end of a word, are sometimes pronounced if the following word starts with a **vowel sound** or **a mute [h]** as in « **les en**fants ».

7 In the following examples, indicate whether there is or not a liaison by ticking the right answer Y (✓) or N (✗).

Sentence	Y	N
Un homme		
Les élèves		
Les haricots		

Sentence	Y	N
Les vieux éléphants		
Le petit ami		
Les yeux		

8 Complete the following crosswords using words learnt in this chapter.

	1	2	3	4	5	6	7	8	9	10
A										
B										
C										
D										
E										
F										
G										
H										
I										
J										

Vertically
1. Polite form of "you"
4. A lot of
5. Something that you say
6. Number
8. The opposite of woman – mother
10. A very happy woman

Horizontally
B. A greeting
C. Short conjunction
E. Informal greeting
G. The opposite of hot
H. What you are at school
I. Too much

9 Find and correct the 10 mistakes in the text below.

« Mon pere est rentre hier soir du Venezuela pour feter Noel en famille. Il veut des festivites francaises ! C'est genial d'etre enfin ensemble ! C'est l'heure des cadeaux et des escargots ! Nous allons nous regaler ! Quelle fete cela sera ! »

Congratulations! You have completed chapter 1! It is now time to add up the icons and write the results on page 128 for your final assessment.

2
Around Articles & Nouns

The forms of nouns

- In French, nearly all nouns are masculine (*m.* or *nm.* in dictionaries) or feminine (*f.* or *nf.*). Most feminine nouns end in **[–e] (une fill<u>e</u>)** while most masculine nouns end with a consonant **(un garç<u>on</u>)**.
  However, there are, as always, a lot of exceptions **(<u>un arbre</u>)** and in reality, the gender of most nouns just needs to be checked in a dictionary and learnt. So remember to always learn the noun with its gender!
  Additionally, many nouns have different masculine and feminine forms such as « **un homme** » (*a man*) and « **une femme** » (*a woman*) for example.

- To form the plural (*pl.*), all you need is to add an **[–s]** to the end of the noun (**une fille → <u>des</u> fill<u>es</u>**), sometimes an **–x** or **–ux** (**un cheveu → <u>des</u> cheveu<u>x</u> ; un journal → <u>des</u> journ<u>aux</u>**).   If the noun already ends in S, X, or Z, then there is no difference between the singular and plural form (**le fil<u>s</u> → les fil<u>s</u>**).

I Tick the right answer: are the following words masculine (M), feminine (F) or plural (P)?

Nouns	M	F	P
Salon	○	○	○
Chambre	○	○	○
Toilettes	○	○	○
Cave	○	○	○
Grenier	○	○	○
Cuisine	○	○	○

Complete the following grid (using a dictionary if necessary).

Masculine Singular	Feminine Singular	Masculine Plural
....	Une amie	....
Un Français	....	....
....	....	Des marchands
Un marié	....	....
....	Une avocate	....
....	....	Des invités

The definite articles

The definite article **"the"** has four forms in French. The form of the definite article varies according to the word it precedes:

- « **Le** » before a masculine noun: **le père.**
- « **La** » before a feminine noun: **la mère.**
- « **L'** » before a singular noun starting with a vowel or a silent [h]: **l'enfant, l'hôtel.**
- « **Les** » before a plural noun: **les parents.**

Gender	Singular	Plural
Masculine	**le, l'**	**les**
Feminine	**la, l'**	**les**

 Circle the right definite article.

a. **(Le / La / L' / Les)** maison est grande !

b. **(Le / La / L' / Les)** filles sont très jolies !

c. **(Le / La / L' / Les)** enfants sont gentils.

d. **(Le / La / L' / Les)** eau est trop froide !

e. **(Le / La / L' / Les)** garçon joue au football.

f. **(Le / La / L' / Les)** homme est très grand !

4 Match the definite article with the corresponding noun.

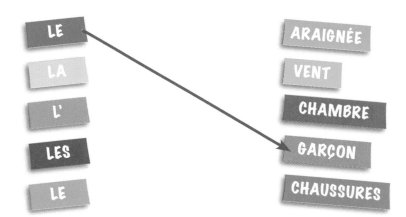

LE	ARAIGNÉE
LA	VENT
L'	CHAMBRE
LES	GARÇON
LE	CHAUSSURES

The indefinite articles

- « **Un** » and « **une** » are the equivalent of the English article *a*. « **Un** » is used in front of a masculine noun whereas « **une** » is used in front of a feminine noun: **un arbre** (*a tree*), **une maison** (*a house*).
- The article « **des** » is used in front of plural forms: **des frères** (*brothers*).

Gender	Singular	Plural
Masculine	**un**	**des**
Feminine	**une**	**des**

5 Circle the right indefinite article. You can use a dictionary to find out whether the noun is feminine or masculine.

a. Il y a **(un / une / des)** chat sur le toit.

b. As-tu **(un / une / des)** crayons dans ta trousse ?

c. Je mange **(un / une / des)** gâteaux tous les jours.

d. Il veut **(un / une / des)** guitare pour Noël.

e. Nous avons **(un / une / des)** chien.

The partitive articles

The partitive articles in French correspond to "some" or "any" in English. They are used when referring to an indeterminate quantity. If in English, "some" and "any" can often be omitted, the partitive article is ALWAYS required in French ("**I have Ø friends.**" = « **J'ai des amis.** »)

There are four forms:

- « **Du** » before a masculine noun : **du café.**
- « **De la** » before a feminine noun : **de la salade.**
- « **De l'** » before a singular noun starting with a vowel or a silent [h]: **de l'eau.**
- « **Des** » before a plural noun: **des biscuits.**

Gender	Singular	Plural
Masculine	du/ de l'	des
Feminine	de la/ de l'	des

---

6 **Order your pizza using the right articles from the pizza box!** ••

« *Garçon, s'il vous plaît ! Je voudrais .... pizza avec .... champignons, ... jambon et .... sauce tomate. Je veux .... pizza rapidement car j'ai très faim ! J'aimerais aussi .... eau ! Merci !* »

de la une la de l' du des

The indefinite and partitive articles with the negative form and adjectives

- Note that, as a general rule, if the indefinite and partitive articles are used with the negative form « **un** », « **une** », « **du** », « **de la** », « **de l'** », « **des** » are replaced by « **de** » or « **d'** » : J'ai <u>une</u> voiture → Je n'ai pas <u>de</u> voiture ; J'ai <u>des</u> amis → Je n'ai pas <u>d'</u>amis.
- « **Des** » is usually replaced by « **de** » before an adjective that precedes a plural noun : **J'ai <u>des</u> chaussettes.** → **J'ai <u>de</u> jolies chaussettes**.

7 Turn the following sentences into the negative form.

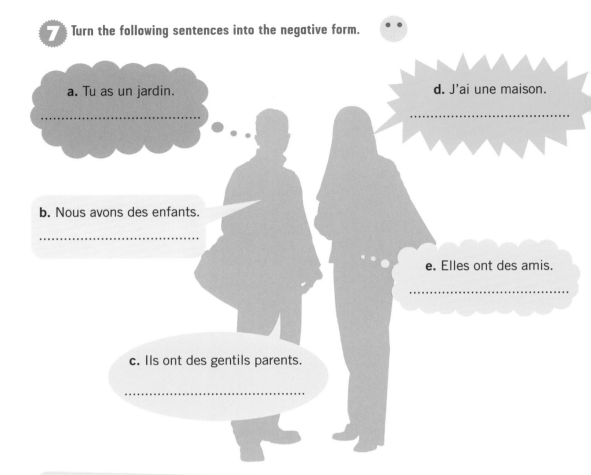

a. Tu as un jardin.
....

d. J'ai une maison.
....

b. Nous avons des enfants.
....

e. Elles ont des amis.
....

c. Ils ont des gentils parents.
....

Feminine or Masculine nouns: people and jobs

- The gender of nouns referring to persons and animals is obvious. If the person or animal is a male then we will use « **un** » or « **le** » and if it is a female then we will use « **une** » or « **la** »: <u>Un</u> **homme** (*A man*) – <u>Une</u> **femme** (*A woman*) – <u>Le</u> **père** (*The father*) – <u>La</u> **mère** (*The mother*) – <u>Le</u> **chat** (*The cat*/male) – <u>La</u> **chatte** (*The cat*/female).

- In general, the feminine form is made by adding an **–e** to the masculine noun. But some nouns' endings undergo a more drastic change (**-er** → **-ère** ; **-en** → **-enne** ; **-an** → **-anne** ; **-on** → **-onne** ; **-eur** → **-euse** ; **-eur** → **-rice** ; **-at** → **-atte** ; **-f** → **-ve** ; **-x** → **-se**). Others, especially nouns referring to occupations, can be used with a masculine form even when referring to a woman (**un docteur**). Or the noun form can be the same for either (**un/une élève**).

8 In the list below, match the occupation in French with its English translation:

un avocat	a waiter
un chanteur	a singer
un professeur	a writer
un serveur	a lawyer
un concierge	an engineer
un écrivain	a caretaker
un ingénieur	a teacher

9 With the help of a dictionary, find the masculine or feminine equivalent to the following nouns.

Masculine	Feminine	Masculine	Feminine
Un vendeur	....	Un maître	....
....	Une musicienne	Un paysan	....
Un acteur	....	....	Une secrétaire
....	Une boulangère	Un dentiste	....
....	Une étudiante	Un professeur	....

Congratulations! You have completed chapter 2! It is now time to add up the icons and write the results on page 128 for your final assessment.

3

Around Pronouns Part 1
A pronoun is a word used instead of a noun

Subject pronouns

- The subject of a verb is the person or thing doing the action of the verb. A subject pronoun replaces this person or thing (eg. **Gaston aime les frites → Il aime les frites.**)

- The various French subject pronouns are as follow:

SINGULAR		PLURAL	
Je/j'	*I*	**Nous**	*We*
Tu	*You (familiar/informal)*	**Vous**	*You (group or polite/formal)*
Il	*He, it*	**Ils**	*They*
Elle	*She, it*	**Elles**	*They*
On	*One, we, they*		

- Note that:

  - **Je** becomes **J'** in front of a vowel or silent **h** (eg. **J'ai un frère.**)

  - **Tu** and **Vous** both mean *you*: however, **Tu** is used when talking to friends, family or someone close. It is an informal form. **Vous** is used when talking to a group of people or to one person but in a formal manner, which means that it is not always plural.

  - **Il/Elle** and **Ils/Elles**: they are used to refer to things, animals or people. They agree in gender and number with the noun they replace. However, **Ils** is used to refer to several nouns of various gender.

  - **On** is used in the sense of "*you*" or "*people*", of "*someone*" or instead of **nous.**

1 Translate the English subject pronouns below into French.

a. *(You/singular)* .... es très grande !

b. *(She)* .... a quarante-cinq ans.

c. *(We)* .... sommes Canadiens.

d. *(They/fem)* .... adorent les araignées !

e. *(You/plural)* .... êtes très élégantes !

2 Fill in the blanks using the appropriate subject pronoun from the gift box below:

a. .... sont au Kenya.

b. .... êtes au cinéma ?

c. .... est heureuse.

d. .... sommes à la boulangerie.

e. .... suis allergique au pollen.

Auxiliary verbs Être (*to be*) & Avoir (*to have*) in the present tense

The present tense is used to describe a current situation.

ÊTRE		AVOIR	
I am	**Je suis**	*I have*	**J'ai**
You are (singular/informal)	**Tu es**	*You have* (singular/informal)	**Tu as**
He/It is	**Il est**	*He/It has*	**Il a**
She/It is	**Elle est**	*She/It has*	**Elle a**
We are	**Nous sommes**	*We have*	**Nous avons**
You are (plural/formal)	**Vous êtes**	*You have* (plural/formal)	**Vous avez**
They are	**Ils sont** (masc.) **Elles sont** (fem.)	*They have*	**Ils ont** (masc.) **Elles ont** (fem.)

3 Complete the following sentences using the right form of BE (ÊTRE).

a. Il .... peintre.

b. Nous .... étudiants.

c. Elles .... actrices.

d. Vous .... boulangers ?

e. Je .... traducteur.

4 Complete the following sentences using the right form of HAVE (AVOIR).

a. J'... 45 ans.

b. Nous .... un chien.

c. Ils .... 3 vélos.

d. Tu .... une moto ?

e. Elle .... 2 maisons.

5 Complete the following sentences using the right form of either BE (ÊTRE) or HAVE (AVOIR).

a. Philippe .... ingénieur.

b. Karine .... un chien et deux hamsters.

c. Clémentine .... très jolie.

d. Nicolas .... gentil.

e. Oriane .... une belle robe.

6 Underline the right subject pronoun.

a. Il / Elle / Tu
est courageuse.

c. Il / Vous / Nous
sommes en Australie.

e. Je / Il / Tu
suis Belge.

b. Vous / Tu / J'
avez une belle voiture !

d. Elles / Ils / Vous
sont petits.

Direct Object Pronouns

• The direct object of the verb is the thing or person having the action done to it/them. Direct pronouns are placed in front of the verb: **Xavier me voit** *(Xavier sees me)*.

• French direct pronouns are:

ENGLISH	FRENCH
me	**me/m'**
you (singular)	**te/t'**
him/it	**le/l'**
her/it	**la/l'**
us	**nous**
you (plural/polite)	**vous**
them	**les**

The direct object pronoun for « **on** » is « **vous** ».

• **M', t', l'** are used when in front of a vowel.

• Indirect pronouns are used with verbs that require an indirect object. These pronouns are mostly used with verbs meaning giving, telling, offering or showing. They are used to say that something is done to or for someone:
They are telling you to stop → **Ils te disent d'arrêter.**

7 Complete the following sentences, using the appropriate direct object pronoun.

a. Je .... aime ! *(her)*

b. Tu .... attends quelques minutes ? *(me)*

c. Elles .... ont invités au restaurant. *(us)*

d. Je .... ai vus au cinéma. *(you, plural)*

e. Stéphanie .... attend depuis une heure. *(you, singular)*

8 Underline the correct answer. Two correct answers are sometimes possible!

a. Marc le prend tous les jours. ➜ le train / la voiture

b. Il l'adore ! ➜ Maéva / Bruno

c. Tu la ranges dans quel tiroir ? ➜ la fourchette / le couteau

d. Elle les voit tous les week-ends. ➜ ses cousins / ses cousines

e. Il vous comprend très bien. ➜ toi et ton amie / Adèle et Catherine

Indirect Object Pronouns

- French Indirect pronouns are:

ENGLISH	FRENCH
me	**me/m'**
you (singular)	**te/t'**
him/it	**lui**
her/it	**lui**
us	**nous**
you (plural/polite)	**vous**
them	**leur**

- When an action is directed "toward" or "at" an object, then that object is called an "Indirect Object". An Indirect Object Pronoun takes the place of an Indirect Object Noun:

Sophie parle à Jérôme.
(*Sophie speaks to whom./*<u>*à qui ?*</u>)

→ **Sophie <u>lui</u> parle.**
(<u>**lui**</u> takes the place of Jérôme = *Sophie speaks to him*).

Sophie	parle	à	Jérôme
subject	*verb = action*	*preposition*	*Noun*

Sophie	lui	parle	
subject	*Indirect object pronoun = replaces Jérôme*	*verb = action*	

9 Complete the following sentences, using the appropriate Indirect Object Pronoun.

a. Il a dit bonjour à Sophie. ➜ Il .... a dit bonjour.

b. J'ai donné une lettre à toi et à ton frère. ➜ Je...................... ai donné une lettre.

c. Marie pose une question à toi et à moi. ➜ Marie .... pose une question.

d. Elle téléphone à son père tous les dimanches. ➜ Elle .... téléphone tous les dimanches.

e. Ton père a répondu (à toi). ➜ Ton père.. a répondu.

Direct or Indirect? Fill in the following crossword by completing the sentences below with the appropriate object pronoun.

1→ Il .... *(her)* a répondu oui!

2→ Je .... *(you, plural)* ai écris une lettre.

3→ Vous ......*(us)* indiquez la mauvaise direction !

4→ Tu .... *(us)* parles trop fort !

5→ Angèle .... *(them)* chante une chanson.

6→ Je .... *(her)* vois dans la cuisine.

7→ Elles ..... *(him)* racontent une longue histoire.

8→ Marcelle veut .... *(you, polite)* voir.

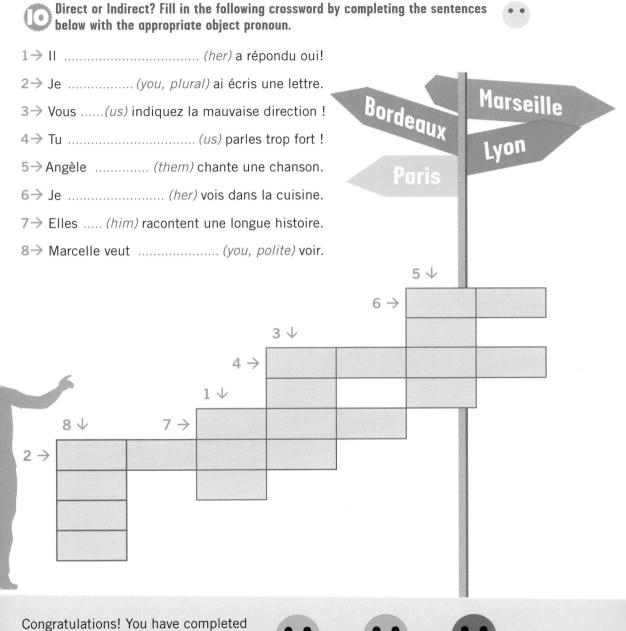

Congratulations! You have completed chapter 3! It is now time to add up the icons and write the results on page 128 for your final assessment.

4

Around Adjectives

Descriptive/Qualifying Adjectives – Nationalities and Colours

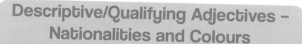

- An adjective is a word that modifies a noun or a pronoun by describing it. In French, unlike in English, adjectives agree in gender (feminine or masculine) and number (singular or plural) with the nouns that they modify.

- Look at the four following possible forms:

	Singular	Plural
Masculine	Joli	Jolis
Feminine	Jolie	Jolies

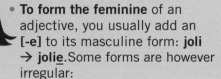

- **To form the feminine** of an adjective, you usually add an **[-e]** to its masculine form: **joli → jolie**. Some forms are however irregular:

  - If the masculine form already ends with an **[e]**, then it does not change in the feminine: **Il est triste. → Elle est triste.**

- Some of the most irregular changes which occur from the masculine to the feminine are :

  [-n] → [-nne]   **[-eur] → [-rice]**
  [-c] → [-que]   **[-f] → [-ve]**
  [-l] → [-lle]   **[-c]/[-s] → [-che]**
  [-er] → [-ère]   **[-g] → [-gue]**
  [-et] → [-ète]   **[-x] → [-se]**
  [-et] → [-ette]   **[-u] → [-üe]**
  [-eur] → [-euse]

- And for many adjectives, the feminine form is different altogether (**vieux → vieille ; fou → folle**). You will need to learn those as you go!

- **To form the plural,** you usually add an **[-s]** to the singular form: **joli → jolis**.
  - If the singular form already ends in **[-s]** or **[-x]**, then it remains the same.
  - If its singular form is **[-al]**, then it usually will change to **[-aux]**
  - and if it is **[-eau]**, it will change to **[-eaux]**.

I Complete the following table.

Masculine Singular	Feminine Singular	Masculine Plural	Feminine Plural
Français	Française	....	Françaises
....	Mexicaine	Mexicains	Mexicaines
Grand	Grande	Grands	....
Gros	Grosse	....	Grosses
Poli	....	Polis	Polies
Beau	Belle	Beaux	....
Bon	....	Bons	Bonnes
....	Vieille	Vieux	Vieilles

2 Fill in the blanks in the following sentences by choosing the appropriate adjective in the box below.

patient   méchants   gentille
amoureux   maladroits   bavardes

a.
Quelle générosité ! Elle est vraiment très
.... !

b.
Fais très attention. Ces chiens sont
....

c.
Sois .... Sébastien. Ton tour viendra !

d.
Regarde ces deux femmes là-bas ! Elles sont vraiment
.... !

e.
Oh Marceau, avec un tel sourire, toi, tu es
.... !

f.
Ils sont tellement
.... !
Ils cassent toujours quelque chose...

- Note that if adjectives usually come before the noun that they modify in English, most adjectives follow the noun that they modify in French:

a blue house
→ **une maison bleue.**

- Some adjectives however, come before the noun, such as :
– cardinal numbers,
– **beau, bon, court, dernier, gentil, grand, gros, haut, jeune, joli, long, mauvais, nouveau, petit** and **vieux.**

3 Place the adjective in the right place within the following sentences.

a. Oh, regarde ! Quel paysage ! (**beau**)

....

b. J'aime beaucoup cette robe. (**rouge**)

....

c. C'est une fille. (**jalouse**)

....

d. Quel tableau ! (**joli**)

....

e. Je suis fatigué. C'était un voyage. (**long**)

....

Nationalities

- When talking about someone from a particular country, you must use a capital letter: **un <u>A</u>ustralien/les <u>A</u>ustraliens**.
- However, if you are talking about someone or something, you must use a small letter: **la cuisine <u>f</u>rançaise ; les enfants sont <u>a</u>nglais**.
- Nationalities carry a gender: **un <u>A</u>fricain/<u>une</u> Africaine**.
- Note that countries also carry a gender in French: *Finland* = **<u>La</u> Finlande.**

4 Underline the correct form of the following adjectives - Nationalities.

a. Mon ami est anglais / anglaise / anglaises.

b. Cette fille est coréen / coréenne / coréennes.

c. Ses parents sont finlandais / finlandaise / finlandaises.

d. Ce groupe de musique est canadien / canadienne / canadiens / canadiennes.

e. Les joueurs de cette équipe sont chinois / chinoise / chinoises.

f. Les chanteuses de cette chorale sont américain / américaine / américains / américaines.

5 Fill in the following table.

Flags	Masc. Sing.	Fem. Sing.	Masc. Pl.	Fem. Pl.
	Hollandais	Hollandaise	Hollandais	Hollandaises

Colours

Colours which get their name from:
– a fruit (**cerise**, **olive**), flower (**lavande**), gem (**émeraude**) or metal (**argent**),
– or which are in compound forms (**bleu marine**),
do not change in the feminine or in the plural:
Ses chaussures sont <u>marron</u> (*brown/chestnut*). **Elle a des yeux <u>bleu clair</u>** (*light blue*).

6 Fill in the following table.

Colours	Masc. Sing.	Fem. Sing.	Masc. Pl.	Fem. Pl.
	Jaune	Jaune	Jaunes	Jaunes

7 Write the correct form of the adjective in the following sentences.

a. De belles chaussures (bleu)
....

b. De très jolies fleurs (jaune)
....

c. De beaux pulls (marron)
....

d. Une élégante cravate (noir)
....
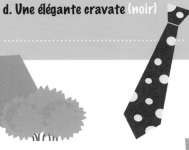

e. Un buisson (vert)
....

Demonstrative Adjectives

- Demonstrative adjectives are used to point out someone or something and agree in gender and number with the noun which follows:

	Singular	Plural
Masculine	Ce, cet	Ces
Feminine	Cette	Ces

- **« Cet »** is used in front of a masculine singular noun or adjective beginning with a vowel or a silent **[h]**:
  <u>cet</u> **ananas** (*pineapple*), <u>cet</u> **habit** (*piece of clothing*).

8 Circle the right demonstrative adjective.

a. J'ai beaucoup aimé (**ce / cet / cette / ces**) film !

b. Quelle horreur ! (**Ce / Cet / Cette / Ces**) pomme était pourrie *(rotten)* !

c. (**Ce / Cet / Cette / Ces**) enfants sont très bruyants *(noisy)*.

d. Peux-tu me passer (**ce / cet / cette / ces**) plat, s'il te plaît ?

e. (**Ce / Cet / Cette / Ces**) homme a une cravate rigolote !

Possessive Adjectives

- Unlike in English, possessive adjectives agree in gender and number with the noun which follow and NOT with the possessor. See the table below:

Masc. Sing.	Fem. Sing.	Plu.
mon	ma	mes
ton	ta	tes
son	sa	ses
notre	notre	nos
votre	votre	vos
leur	leur	leurs

- **Note** that the masculine form is used before a word which starts with a vowel: <u>**mon**</u> **amie Sophie**.

9 Pick the right possessive adjective from the table above for each of the following sentence:

a. As-tu vu .... *(my)* livre ? Je ne le trouve pas !

b. .... *(his)* sœurs sont très grandes !

c. J'adore .... *(their)* chien ! Il est très amusant !

d. .... *(his)* amie s'appelle Éléanore.

e. .... *(your)* père est très gentil Anne !

With parts of the body

When using **avoir** or a reflexive verb (such as **se laver**), the definite article is used, not the possessive adjective:

J'ai les cheveux blonds.
(I have got blond hair.)

Elle s'est lavé les mains.
(She washed her hands.)

10 Translate the following sentences:

a. He has got brown hair.

....

b. His father is French.

....

c. Their cat is white.

....

d. She washed her hair yesterday.

....

e. Your house is very big!

....

Congratulations! You have completed chapter 4! It is now time to add up the icons and write the results on page 128 for your final assessment.

5
Around Comparatives and Superlatives

The Comparative and Adjectives

The comparative is used when comparing two things or two people.

- To express inferiority, you use: **moins ... que ...** = *less ... than ...*
  (eg.: **Karine est <u>moins</u> fatiguée <u>que</u> Coralie.** = *Karine is less tired than Coralie.*)
- To express equality, you use: **aussi ... que ...** = *as ... as ...*
  (eg.: **Sophie est <u>aussi</u> jolie <u>qu'</u>Éloïse.** = *Sophie is as pretty as Éloïse.*)
- To express superiority, you use: **plus ... que** = more ... than ...
  (eg.: **Pierre est <u>plus</u> bavard <u>que</u> Daniel.** = *Pierre is more talkative than Daniel.*)

Note that **que** becomes **qu'** in front of vowels and silent **h** and don't forget that the adjectives must agree with the subjects (i.e. the first of the two items compared).

1 Turn the adjectives between brackets into a comparative according to the symbols (**–** inferiority; **=** equality; **+** superiority) as shown in the example.

Eg.: Mon frère est (grand **+**) <u>plus grand</u> que mon père.

a. Son chat est (rapide **–**) .... son chien !

b. Floriane est (jolie **=**) .... Martine.

c. Ce livre est (intéressant **+**) .... celui-là.

d. Laurent est (gentil **–**) .... Sylvain.

e. Ta maison est (grande **=**) .... la mienne.

2 Translate the following sentences into English.

a. Cette table est plus grande que celle-là *(that one).*

= ....

b. Alexandre est aussi sportif que Julien.

= ....

c. Sophie est moins jolie que Karine.

= ....

d. Julien est aussi drôle que Lily.

= ....

e. Le sac bleu est plus grand que le sac noir.

= ....

3 In the following examples, underline the right form of the adjectives.

a. Elles sont plus **bavard / bavarde / bavards / bavardes** que nous.

b. Marion est aussi **beau / belle / beaux / belles** que Sophie.

c. Emmanuel est aussi **intelligent / intelligente / intelligents / intelligentes** que Claire.

d. Louis et Gabriel sont moins **gentil / gentille / gentils / gentilles** que Catherine et Jennifer.

e. L'arbre de droite est plus **petit / petite / petits / petites** que l'arbre de gauche.

The Comparative and Adverbs

- The same rules as above apply except that instead of using an adjective, you use an adverb.
- An adverb is a word which modifies an adjective, another adverb or a verb (eg.: **Il écrit lentement.** = *He writes slowly.*)
- Though many adverbs such as **vite** (*quickly*), **bien** (*well*) and **mal** (*badly*) are not formed from another word, many are.
  - The most usual way to form an adverb from an existing adjective is by adding the suffix **-ment** when the adjective's last letter is a vowel (**lent → lentement**); and to the feminine form of the adjective if its masculine form ends with a consonant (**seul → seule → seulement**).
  - There are also some more irregular adverbs such as: **prudent** (*Careful*) → **prudemment** (*Carefully*); **énorme** (*Enormous*) → **énormément** (*Enormously*); **meilleur** (*Better*) → **mieux** (*Better*); **gentil** (*Kind*) → **gentiment** (*Kindly*).

4 Adjective or Adverb? Put the words in the box in the right column.

Adjectives	Adverbs

FACILEMENT   **Belle**   Rapidement

Gentil   **Mieux**   **Malheureusement**

5 Following the rules in the box above, turn the following adjectives into adverbs.

Eg.: Heureux ➜ Heureusement

a. Rare ➜ ....

b. Poli ➜ ....

c. Courageux ➜ .... ➜ ....

d. Prudent ➜ ....

e. Parfait ➜ .... ➜ ....

The Superlative

- The superlative is used when expressing that something or someone is the -est or the most or the least. You just need to use the appropriate definite article **le, la** or **les** in front of the adverbs « **plus** » or « **moins** »

- Like all adjectives, the adjectives used with the superlative agree with the nouns that they modify (eg.: **Les pommes les plus rouges.**)

- Note that when the adjective comes after the noun, the article (**le, la** or **les**) is repeated (eg.: **C'est le restaurant le plus cher de la ville.**)

- Also, after a superlative, « **de** » is used to express "in": *Julian is the most intelligent in the class* = **Julian est le plus intelligent de la classe**.

6 Circle the appropriate article in the following sentences.

a. C'est le / la / les plus belle maison du quartier.

b. Ce sont les garçons le / la / les plus polis de la classe !

c. Ce sont le / la / les robes les plus laides du magasin.

d. C'est le / la / les chien le plus méchant du parc.

e. C'est le / la / les fille la plus jolie du village.

7 In the following sentences using the superlative form, write the right form of the adjective.

a. Ces fleurs sont les plus (coloré) .... du jardin.

b. Elle est la plus (active) .... de sa classe.

c. Ce bébé est le plus (mignon) .... que je connaisse.

d. Leurs voitures sont les plus (propre) .... de la rue !

e. Jeanne est la femme la plus (maladroit) .... !

8 Fill the blanks with the appropriate article or with the preposition « de ».

a. C'est la maison .... plus chère du quartier.

b. Sophie est la fille .... moins sportive du groupe.

c. Jonathan est le garçon le plus rapide .... son club.

d. Les dattes sont les fruits .... plus sucrés.

e. Joséphine est la plus maligne .... l'école.

Irregular forms

- The superlative is more often used with adjectives, but can also be used with adverbs.

- The adjective **mauvais** (*bad*) becomes **pire** (*worse*) and not **le plus mauvais***:
  * forme incorrecte

Il est <u>pire</u> que moi. = *He is worse than me.*

- It becomes **le pire** in the superlative: **C'est la pire semaine de ma vie !** = *It is the worse week of my life!*

- The adjective **bon** (*good*) becomes **meilleur** (*better*) in the comparative.

- The adverb **bien** (*well*) becomes **mieux** (*better*) in the comparative and **le mieux** (*the best*) in the superlative.

9 In the following sentences, write the appropriate comparative or superlative form.

Eg.: Noah est (+ mignon) <u>le plus mignon</u> de sa classe.

a. Élisa est (= étourdie) ....Vanessa.

b. C'est (+ bon) .... gâteau du menu.

c. Ils sont (+ timides) .... leurs parents.

d. Audrey est la fille (+ généreuse) .... que je connaisse.

e. Ce livre est (- mauvais)........................... que j'aie jamais lu !

Congratulations! You have completed chapter 5! It is now time to add up the icons and write the results on page 128 for your final assessment.

Around Sentence and Forms

Affirmative Sentences

The most common pattern in a French affirmative sentence is:
Subject + Verb + Object:

Je	**regarde**	**un film de science-fiction.**
Subject	*Verb*	*Complement*

Place the sentence segments in the right column.
Eg.: Je vais au cinéma.

a. Il mange du gâteau.

b. Nous avons vu Charles et Simon.

c. Vous chantez une belle mélodie.

d. Elle donne des bonbons !

e. Nous aimons les films de science-fiction.

	Subject	Verb	Complement
	Je	vais	au cinéma.
a.			
b.			
c.			
d.			
e.			

2 **Put the following segments into the right order so as to form a sentence.**
Eg.: suis / France / Je / en /. → Je suis en France.

a. au restaurant / a invité / Julie / ses amis /.

....

b. voiture / une / Sylvain / nouvelle / a acheté /.

....

c. Son / très / est / pull / joli /.

....

d. en / voyage / train / Christian / souvent /.

....

e. à 8 heures / prend / Léon / petit / son / déjeuner /.

....

Negative Constructions

- Some of the most common negative constructions are **ne + verb + any of the following:**
  - **Pas =** Not: Nous **n'**avons **pas** de chien. = *We haven't got a dog.*
  - **Rien =** Nothing/Anything: Je **ne** sais **rien**. = *I don't know anything.*
  - **Plus =** No/Any longer/Anymore: Solène **ne** boude **plus**. = *Solène is no longer sulking.*
  - **Aucun/Aucune =** not, not one, any: Il **n'**a **aucun** ami. = *He hasn't got any friend.*
  - **Jamais =** Never: Je ne suis **jamais** allé en Belgique. = *I have never been to Belgium.*
  - **Ni ... ni ... =** Neither ... nor ...: **Elle n'aime ni les pommes ni les poires.** = *She neither likes apples nor pears.*

- Note that **ne** becomes **n'** before a vowel or a silent **h**. Il **n'**habite **pas** **chez ses parents**.

- In the perfect tense, the negative form wraps around the auxiliary (except with **ne ... personne** and **ne ... que**): Il **n'a jamais** vu ce film. = He has never seen this movie.

3 Fill in the blanks with the appropriate negative construction.

Eg. Je ..... ai ...... de voiture (not) → Je **n'ai pas** de voiture

a. Estelle ...... est .... malade. **(any longer)**

b. Martine .... a .... chat ...... chien. **(neither...nor)**

c. Stéphanie .... est .... méchante. **(not)**

d. Roger .... a .... mangé de calamar. **(never)**

e. Julian .... a .... bu hier soir. **(anything)**

4 Turn the following assertions into negative sentences.

a. Achille aime les fraises.

→ ....

b. Violette joue au tennis.

→ ....

c. Romain est blond.

→ ....

d. Séverine adore les films d'aventure.

→ ....

e. Olivier est petit.

→ ....

Interrogative Form

- **Direct questions (yes/no answers):** the subject and the verb can be inverted but do not have to be. Eg.: **Es-tu content ?** – **Tu es content ?** = *Are you happy?*

- **Note**: If the verb ends in a vowel with il/elle/on, you will need to add **-t**: **A-t-elle un chat ?**

- **Est-ce que... ?:** to ask a direct question, you can also put **est-ce que** in front of the subject: **Est-ce que tu es content ?** = *Are you happy?*

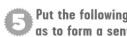 Put the following segments into the right order so as to form a sentence.

Eg.: suis / France / Je / en / Est-ce que / ?
→ Est-ce que je suis en France ?

a. les poires / Ginette / Est-ce que / aime / ?

→ ....

b. le chinois / elle / parle / Françoise / -t- / ?

→ ....

c. Australie / que / Marine / Est / en / ? / -ce / vit

→ ....

d. voir / Peut / venir / -il / me / ?

→ ....

e. -elle / mon / écouter / Veut / CD / ?

→ ....

 Turn the following statements into questions with « est-ce que ».

Eg. Elle aime le gâteau. → Est-ce qu'elle aime le gâteau ?

a. Il déteste les chats.

→ .... ?

b. Tu vas au cinéma.

→ .... ?

c. Vous regardez la télé.

→ .... ?

d. Ils sont allés en Italie.

→ .... ?

e. Elle aime ma confiture.

→ .... ?

Questions starting with a question word

- These are questions which require a complete answer (not just yes or no). **Où vas-tu ?** = *Where are you going?* – **Je vais au cinéma.** = *I am going to the cinema.*

- **Note**: if the question is negative, just put **ne** in front of the verb and **pas** after. **Ne** becomes **n'** in front of a vowel or silent h. Eg.: **Ne mangez-vous pas de tarte ?** = *Don't you eat pie?* – **N'aimez-vous pas l'opéra ?** = *Don't you like opera?*

Question Words List *(Les mots interrogatifs):*

ENGLISH	FRENCH	ENGLISH	FRENCH
Who	Qui	Where	Où
Whom with	Avec qui	Why	Pourquoi
What	Que Qu'est-ce que Quoi	How	Comment
		How much/ How many	Combien
Which	Quel/Quelle/Quels/ Quelles	How long	Combien de temps
When	Quand	At what time	À quelle heure

7 Fill in the blanks with the appropriate question word.

a. .... son train arrive-t-il à la gare ?

b. .... a mangé mon yaourt ?

c. .... ce collier coûte-t-il ?

d. .... es-tu rentré ? Tu avais oublié la clé !

e. .... fait-il dans sa chambre ?

8 Ask the question corresponding to the answer.

Eg.: Quand viens-tu me voir ?
→ Tu viens me voir vendredi.

a. .... ?
→ Je vais bien merci !

b. .... ?
→ Il habite à Paris.

c. .... ?
→ Le film a duré 110 minutes.

d. .... ?
→ Sophie est rentrée parce qu'elle était fatiguée.

e. .... ?
→ C'est Louis qui a cassé le vase.

Differences between English and French

- Adjectives generally come after the noun unlike in English: **Elle porte une robe verte.** = *She is wearing a green dress.*

- Adverbs usually come after the verb: **Il ne va jamais en Italie.** = *He never goes to Italy.*

9 Translate the following sentences.

a. I never go to the theatre. → ....

b. Who took my book? → ....

c. When is she coming back home? → ....

d. I prefer the blue trousers. → ....

e. He doesn't want to go out tonight. → ....

10 Fill in the following telephone conversation using what you have learnt in this lesson.

« Allô, Louise ? __ es-tu ?
Nous sommes inquiets. Nous __ savons (know)
___ où tu es. _____
tu fais ? _____ n'as-tu pas téléphoné ?
__ recommence _____ (never) ! »

Congratulations! You have completed chapter 6! It is now time to add up the icons and write the results on page 128 for your final assessment.

Around Pronouns Part 2
Reflexive Pronouns and Verbs, Possessive, Interrogative and Relative Pronouns & En/Y

Reflexive Pronouns

Reflexive pronouns are part of reflexive verbs (**se voir, se parler, s'aimer**). They mean "*myself*", "*yourself*". They "reflect" the subject: *They love each other.* → **Ils s'aiment**.

ENGLISH	FRENCH
me	**me/m'**
you (singular)	**te/t'**
him/it	**se/s'**
her/it	**se/s'**
us	**nous**
you (plural/polite)	**vous**
them	**se**

Note: it is sometimes only implied in English. He washes (himself) every morning. → **Il se lave tous les matins**.

Reflexive Verbs

Reflexive verbs are verbs which express an action that reflects the subject. **Je me présente.** = *I am introducing myself*. They form their perfect tense with être and the past participle.

nous

se

s'

vous

te

me

1 Fill in the blanks using the reflexive pronouns from the box. Beware! There is one too many!

a. Elle .... réveille à 7 heures tous les matins.

b. Je .... rappelle de Bruno.

c. Nous .... sommes encore disputés.

d. Vous .... téléphonez souvent ?

e. Il ne .... est pas rasé ce matin.

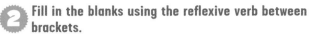 **Fill in the blanks using the reflexive verb between brackets.**

a. Elle .... très tôt le mardi matin. (**se lever**)

b. Je .... toujours en jean ! (**s'habiller**)

c. Il ne .... jamais. Quelle horreur ! (**se laver**)

d. Nous ....
beaucoup ! Vive les vacances ! (**s'amuser**)

e. Vous ....
à quelle heure le samedi soir ? (**se coucher**)

Demonstrative pronouns

The different forms of **celui** (*the one*) are demonstrative pronouns:

	Singular	Plural
Masculine	celui	ceux
Feminine	celle	celles

These pronouns are used either:

- With a preposition such as **à, de, dans** + noun: **J'aime cette maison mais je n'aime pas <u>celle</u> de mes parents.** = *I like this house but I don't like my parents' (one).*

- With a relative pronoun such as **qui**: **Celui <u>qui</u> est venu hier.** = The one who came yesterday.

- With (and before) **-ci** and **-là**:

	Masculine	Feminine	English
Singular	celui-ci	celle-ci	this one
	celui-là	celle-là	that one
Plural	ceux-ci	celles-ci	these ones
	ceux-là	celles-là	those ones

- **Ce (c')** is the neutral form of **celui**. It is used in front of a relative pronoun (**ce que/ce qui**) and in the expression **c'est**.

- **Ceci** and **Cela (ça)**: *this* and *that*. **<u>Cela</u> n'est pas vrai.** = *That is not true.* These pronouns do not change in number and gender.

3 Match the noun with its corresponding demonstrative pronoun.

Les montres	●	●	**Celles**
L'enfant	●	●	**Celui**
La chambre	●	●	**Ceux**
Les jupes	●	●	**Celles**
Le manteau	●	●	**Celui**
Les livres	●	●	**Celle**

4 Write the correct form of the pronoun written into brackets.

Eg.: J'adore ces boucles d'oreilles. Lesquelles ? → Celles-là (*those ones*).

a. Je veux voir ce film. Lequel ? → .... (*this one*)

b. J'aimerais une baguette, s'il vous plaît. Laquelle ? → .... (*this one*)

c. As-tu lu les livres de Bernard Werber ? Lesquels ? → .... (*those ones*)

d. As-tu amené le dossier? Lequel ? → .... (*that one*)

e. Nous voulons visiter beaucoup de pays. Lesquels ? → .... (*these ones*)

Interrogative Pronouns

- **Qui/Que :** **Qui** is the question word standing for *Who/Whom* and **Que** stands for *What*.

- **Quel** stands for *Which* or *What* when followed by a noun as in **Quelle heure est-il ?** = *What time is it?* It agrees with the noun it refers to: **Quel jour ? Quelle voiture ? Quels livres ? Quelles couleurs ?** = *What day? Which car? Which books? What colours?*

	Singular	Plural
Masculine	Quel	Quels
Feminine	Quelle	Quelles

- **Lequel** stands for *Which one*. It also agrees with the noun it refers to:

	Singular	Plural
Masculine	Lequel	Lesquels
Feminine	Laquelle	Lesquelles

5 QUI or QUE : choose the appropriate interrogative pronoun.

a. .... fais-tu dans la cuisine ?

b. .... a pris mon manteau ?

c. .... veut-il faire ce soir ?

d. .... est ce jeune homme ?

e. .... a apporté le gâteau ?

quelles
quel
lequel
quelle
laquelle
lesquelles

6 Fill in the blanks using the pronouns given in the hat. Beware! There is one too many!

« .... robe veux-tu mettre aujourd'hui ?
– Je ne sais pas. Celle qui est jolie.

– .... ?
– La bleue.

– Et .... chaussures veux-tu porter ?
– Celles qui sont confortables.

– Mais .... ?
– Les sandales.

– Et .... chapeau aimerais-tu ?
– Celui avec une fleur. Merci ! »

Possessive Pronouns

- French possessive pronouns have got a masculine singular, feminine singular, masculine plural and feminine plural forms.

- A possessive pronoun takes the place of a possessive adjective + noun: **Ma montre** (*my watch*) → **La mienne** (*mine*). Possessive pronouns agree in gender and number with what it is replacing.

- The various French possessive pronouns are:

ENGLISH	FRENCH
mine	le mien, la mienne les miens, les miennes
yours (singular)	le tien, la tienne les tiens, les tiennes
his/hers	le sien, la sienne les siens, les siennes
ours	le nôtre, la nôtre les nôtres
yours (plural/ polite)	le vôtre, la vôtre, les vôtres
theirs	le leur, la leur les leurs

7 Choose the appropriate possessive pronoun as shown in the example below.

Eg.: J'aime mon beau blouson ! → J'aime le mien.

a. J'aime leur belle voiture → J'aime ....

b. J'aime son beau sac à main → J'aime ....

c. J'aime nos beaux chaussons → J'aime ....

d. J'aime ta jolie robe → J'aime ....

e. J'aime ses superbes chaussures → J'aime ....

Relative Pronouns

A relative pronoun is a word that refers to something that comes before (= an antecedent). It can be a word or a sentence and links a noun or a pronoun to the next sentence.

- « **Qui** » and « **Que** » are relative pronouns meaning "*which*", "*that*" or "*who*": *I have a new car which goes very fast!* → **J'ai une nouvelle voiture qui va très vite !** – *The book that I read is great!* → **Le livre que j'ai lu est génial !**

- **Qui** is the subject of the verb which follows: **L'homme qui était dans la rue.** = *The man who was in the street.*

- **Que** is the direct object: **Le film qu'Aurélie regarde.** = *The movie that Aurélie is watching.*

- If instead of replacing a word, you want to replace a whole sentence, then you must use « **ce que** » or « **ce qui** »: *She never stops talking, which I find really annoying.* → **Elle ne s'arrête jamais de parler, ce que je trouve très énervant.**

8 QUI or QUE? Circle the right answer in the following sentences.

a. L'enfant **que / qui** pleurait était perdu.

b. Le dernier film **que / qui** j'ai vu était merveilleux.

c. La tarte **que / qui** maman a préparée est délicieuse !

d. Je connais la femme **que / qui** est devant la boutique.

e. Je déteste le parfum **que / qui** tu portes aujourd'hui.

9 CE QUE or CE QUI ? Circle the right answer in the following sentences.

a. Le bébé a pleuré toute la nuit, **ce que / ce qui** j'ai trouvé fatigant.

b. Il pleut encore, **ce que / ce qui** est très ennuyeux.

c. Je t'ai dit de ranger ta chambre, **ce que / ce qui** je t'ai déjà demandé 3 fois !

d. Le professeur est absent, **ce que / ce qui** signifie que nous pouvons rentrer chez nous.

e. Il a amené des fleurs, **ce que / ce qui** je trouve très gentil.

En / y

- The French pronoun « **en** » is used in place of "of it" or "of them". « **En** » goes in front of the verb: **Combien de films a-t-il ? Il en a 15**. → *How many films has he got? He has got 15 (of them).*

- The French pronoun « **y** » means "there". « **Y** » goes in front of the verb too: *She is going to France next year; she is going there by plane.* → **Elle va en France l'année prochaine ; elle y va en avion.**

- **Note**: in the negative, **ne** becomes **n'** in front of **en** and **y** (vowel): **Je n'en ai pas.** = *I do not have any.*

10 Fill in the blanks with either EN or Y according to the context.

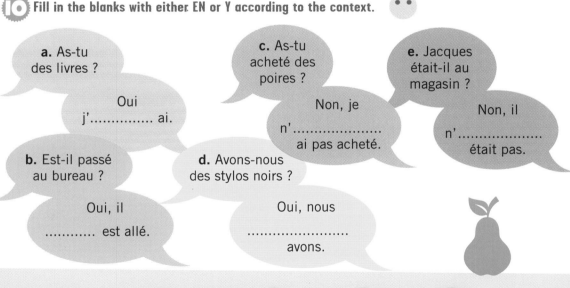

a. As-tu des livres ?

Oui j'.............. ai.

b. Est-il passé au bureau ?

Oui, il .... est allé.

c. As-tu acheté des poires ?

Non, je n'.................... ai pas acheté.

d. Avons-nous des stylos noirs ?

Oui, nous .... avons.

e. Jacques était-il au magasin ?

Non, il n'.................... était pas.

Congratulations! You have completed chapter 7! It is now time to add up the icons and write the results on page 128 for your final assessment.

Around Numbers and Time

Cardinal numbers

Cardinal numbers (cardinaux) are numbers used in counting.

- **Note: Un**: is the only cardinal number which agrees in gender: **Un lapin – Une tortue.**

- **Vingt** and **Cent** take an **s** when not followed by another number and when after a number:
Quatre-vingt<u>s</u> → **Quatre-vingt-<u>douze</u>** ;
Deux cent<u>s</u> → **Deux cent <u>cinquante</u>.**

- **Mille** never takes an **s**.

 Do you remember your cardinal numbers? Fill in the blanks.

1	un/une	19	dix-neuf	80	
2	deux	20	vingt	81	quatre-vingt-un
3	trois	21		82	quatre-vingt-deux
4	quatre	22	vingt-deux	90	
5	cinq	30	trente	91	quatre-vingt-onze
6	six	31	trente et un	92	quatre-vingt-douze
7	sept	32	trente-deux		
8		40	quarante		
9	neuf	41	quarante et un		
10	dix	42	quarante-deux		
11	onze	50			
12	douze	70			
13	treize	74	soixante-quatorze		
14		75	soixante-quinze		
15	quinze	76			
16	seize	77	soixante-dix-sept		
17	dix-sept	78	soixante-dix-huit		
18	dix-huit	79	soixante-dix-neuf		

100	cent
101	cent un
102	cent deux
200	
201	deux cent un
202	deux cent deux
1 000	mille
2 000	
2 001	deux mille un
2 002	deux mille deux
100 000	cent mille
1 000 000	un million

Match the operations on the left to their answers on the right.

2 + 5	=	quatre-vingts
10 x 8	=	vingt et un
9 x 2	=	soixante-treize
10 000 : 10	=	sept
51 + 22	=	soixante-quatorze
30 – 9	=	mille
35 + 39	=	trente-six
216 : 6	=	dix-huit

 One of the following numbers is different from all the others: which one is it?

douze

cinquante-deux

cent quarante-six

cinq cent quatre-vingt-huit

onze

mille huit cents

six

Ordinal numbers

Ordinal numbers show rank or position (first, second, and so on).

Note: the feminine form of « **premier** » is « **première** »: le premier livre que j'ai lu ; la première fille que j'ai vue.

43

Do you remember your ordinal numbers? Fill in the blank:

1ᵉʳ	premier	**12ᵉ**	douzième	**23ᵉ**	vingt-troisième
2ᵉ	deuxième	**13ᵉ**	treizième	**24ᵉ**	vingt-quatrième
3ᵉ	troisième	**14ᵉ**	quatorzième	**25ᵉ**	vingt-cinquième
4ᵉ		**15ᵉ**	quinzième	**26ᵉ**	
5ᵉ	cinquième	**16ᵉ**		**27ᵉ**	vingt-septième
6ᵉ	sixième	**17ᵉ**		**28ᵉ**	vingt-huitième
7ᵉ	septième	**18ᵉ**	dix-huitième	**29ᵉ**	vingt-neuvième
8ᵉ	huitième	**19ᵉ**	dix-neuvième	**30ᵉ**	trentième
9ᵉ		**20ᵉ**	vingtième	**40ᵉ**	quarantième
10ᵉ	dixième	**21ᵉ**		**70ᵉ**	soixante-dixième
11ᵉ	onzième	**22ᵉ**	vingt-deuxième		

100ᵉ	centième
1 000ᵉ	

5 **Unshuffle the following letters in order to find the ordinal numbers!**

a. ÈAURIAMEQTN = _ _ _ _ _ _ _ _ _ _

b. TNGUMENNEÈTCVIVIE = _ _ _ _ _ _ _ _ _ _ _ _ _ _ _ _

c. RREEIMP = _ _ _ _ _ _ _

d. ÈONIEMXISAT = _ _ _ _ _ _ _ _ _ _

e. MMELIÈIL = _ _ _ _ _ _ _ _

f. RITTEÈEMN = _ _ _ _ _ _ _ _ _

Telling the Time

Days and Months are all masculine and do not bear a capital letter (except if placed at the beginning of a sentence).

6 **Do you remember the days of the week?**

Lundi

....

Mercredi

....

Vendredi

....

....

7 **Do you remember the months of the year?**

Janvier

....

Mars

....

Mai

....

Juillet

....

Septembre

....

Novembre

....

8 **Translate the following sentences into English.**

a. J'ai vu Jean-Philippe avant-hier.

= ....

b. Qu'as-tu fait le lendemain ?

= ....

c. Veux-tu aller au cinéma vendredi prochain ?

= ....

d. Ella a vu ce film mardi dernier.

= ....

e. Il fait vraiment beau aujourd'hui !

= ....

Some useful words and phrases

On Monday = **lundi**

On Mondays = **le lundi**

Yesterday = **hier**

Today = **aujourd'hui**

Tomorrow = **demain**

Last Tuesday = **mardi dernier**

Next Thursday = **jeudi prochain**

The day before = **la veille**

The day after = **le lendemain**

The day after tomorrow = **après-demain**

The day before yesterday = **avant-hier**

What time is it? (*Quelle heure est-il ?*)

Il est ... = *It is ...*

midi = *midday*

minuit = *midnight*

deux heures = *two o'clock*

trois heures et quart
= *a quarter past three*

quatre heures et demie
= *half past four*

cinq heures moins le quart
= *a quarter to five*

six heures dix
= *ten past six*

sept heures moins vingt
= *twenty to seven*

À l'heure = *on time*

À temps = *in time*

Un quart d'heure
= *a quarter of an hour*

Une demie-heure
= *a half hour*

À sept heures du matin
= *at seven in the morning*

À sept heures de l'après-midi = *at seven in the afternoon*

À sept heures du soir
= *at seven in the evening*

9 Write the following times next to the clock.

 a. Quelle heure est-il ?
Il est (13h15)

....

 d. Quelle heure est-il ?
Il est (20h40)

....

 b. Quelle heure est-il ?
Il est (16h30)

....

 e. Quelle heure est-il ?
Il est (10h25)

....

 c. Quelle heure est-il ?
Il est (4h45)

....

10 Look at M. Dupouy's agenda and fill in the blanks below writing the adequate times in letters.

Lundi 3 mai	Mardi 4 mai	Mercredi 5 mai
9h00 : *Réunion au bureau*	9h30 : *Rendez-vous Dr Garrant*	8h20 : *Petit déjeuner d'affaires*
	11h00 : *Réunion à La Défense*	
12h30 : *Déjeuner avec M. Gosseaume*	12h20 : *Déjeuner avec Bastian à Montmartre*	13h45 : *Conférence à Dijon*
14h10 : *Présentation nouveau produit*	14h15 : *Aéroport Retour Dijon*	
18h25 : *Aéroport départ pour Paris*	19h00 : *Dîner avec Marie*	18h00 : *Réunion parents d'élèves*

Lundi à _ _ _ _ _ _ _ _ _ _ _ _
M. Dupouy doit se rendre à
une réunion qui a lieu au
bureau. À _ _ _ _ _ _ _ _ _ _ _ _,
il déjeune avec
M. Gosseaume à la Brasserie
Dijonnaise puis
à _ _ _ _ _ _ _ _ _ _ _ _,
il participe à la présentation
du nouveau produit de la
compagnie. Le soir même, à
_ _ _ _ _ _ _ _ _ _ _ _,
il prend l'avion pour Paris.

Le lendemain, M.
Dupouy a un rendez-
vous avec Dr Garrant à
_ _ _ _ _ _ _ _ _ _ _ _, suivi
d'une réunion à La Défense
à _ _ _ _ _ _ _ _ _ _ _ _. Il doit
déjeuner à Montmartre
à _ _ _ _ _ _ _ _ _ _ _ _ avec
son ami Bastian puis se rend
à l'aéroport pour son vol de
_ _ _ _ _ _ _ _ _ _ _ _. Il dîne
avec sa femme, Marie à
_ _ _ _ _ _ _ _ _ _ _ _.

Le mercredi, M. Dupouy
a un déjeuner avec
un collaborateur à
_ _ _ _ _ _ _ _ _ _ _ _ puis doit
se rendre à une conférence
à _ _ _ _ _ _ _ _ _ _ _ _ à Dijon.
À _ _ _ _ _ _ _ _ _ _ _ _, il doit
aller à l'école de son fils pour
rencontrer l'instituteur.

Find the answers to the following riddles.

a. Lundi, Louis dépense la moitié de son argent ; mardi, il dépense le tiers de ce qu'il reste ; mercredi, il a 30 €. Combien avait Louis lundi ?

....

b. Dans sa tirelire, Élise a des pièces de 50 cents et de 20 cents. En tout, elle a 4 €. Combien a-t-elle de pièces de 50 cents sachant qu'il y a 16 pièces en tout ?

....

c. Un fermier a des poules et des lapins. En examinant tous les animaux, il voit 5 têtes et 16 pattes. Combien y a-t-il de lapins et de poules ?

....

d. Marc cuisine 8 tartelettes en 40 minutes. Combien de temps lui faut-il pour préparer 160 tartelettes ?

....

Congratulations! You have completed chapter 8! It is now time to add up the icons and write the results on page 128 for your final assessment.

Around the Perfect Tense

The Infinitive (*L'infinitif*)

- The Infinitive is the basic form of the verb. In English, it contains the preposition "to" in front of the stem: *to love, to finish, to sell*. In French, they are three types of infinitives:
  - first group: **-er (aimer)**.
  - second group: **-ir (finir)**.
  - third group: **-re** or **-oir (vendre, voir)**.

Knowing which group the verb belongs to will help you know how to form all other tenses of the regular verbs.

- **Note:** in order to make an infinitive negative, place **ne pas** in front of it: **ne pas manger**.

- In French, when a verb is followed by another, the second verb must always be in the infinitive: **Je dois aller au bureau**.

1 Write the infinitive form of the following underlined verbs.

a. J'ai <u>mangé</u> trop de gâteaux !

→ ....manger....

b. Ils ont <u>bu</u> toute la limonade !

→ ....boire....

c. Où <u>vas</u>-tu ce matin ?

→ ..aller....

d. Je <u>dormirai</u> dans le salon.

→ ..dormirair....

e. Je <u>voudrais</u> bien gagner au loto !

→ ..vouloir....

2 First, second or third group? Tick the right column:

	1st Group	2nd Group	3rd group
Chanter	☐	☐	☐
Punir	☐	☐	☐
Rendre	☐	☐	☐
Écouter	☐	☐	☐
Pleuvoir	☐	☐	☐
Grandir	☐	☐	☐
Devenir	☐	☐	☐
Danser	☐	☐	☐
Apprendre	☐	☐	☐

Past Participles (*Le participe passé*)

- The past participle of regular verbs is formed by dropping the infinitive ending and adding the appropriate past participle ending, according to the group the verb belongs to.

- Some verbs such as **aller** or **faire** are however irregular.

- The past participle can be used as an adjective (**je suis fatigué**) or a verb (**j'ai vu**).

Regular formation of past participles

	Infinitive	Ending/Type	Drop	Add	Past participle
1st group	Aimer	-er	-er	-é	donné
2nd group	Finir	-ir	-ir	-i	fini
3rd group	Vendre	-re	-re	-u	vendu

 Fill in the following table.

	INFINITIVE	PAST PARTICIPLE
Nous étudions le français.	Étudier	Étudié
a. Il déteste les chats !	....	....
b. Nous dînons généralement tôt.	....	....
c. Elle aime beaucoup le théâtre.	....	....
d. J'écoute mon CD préféré.	....	....
e. Sophie perd régulièrement ses clés !	....	....
f. Prends-tu le train tous les matins ?	....	....

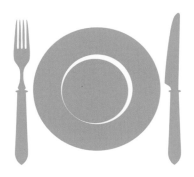

Write the past participle of these irregular verbs.

a. Hier, nous avons
....
(apprendre) une nouvelle leçon !

d. Nous avons
....
(pouvoir) rencontrer le chanteur du groupe.

b. Il m'a
....
(offrir) un magnifique bouquet de roses !

e. Vous avez
....
(faire) vos devoirs ?

c. Elle a
....
(vouloir) rentrer tôt à la maison.

Agreement with « être » and « avoir »

- The past participle of an **avoir** verb only agrees with the direct object when the direct object comes before the verb: **J'ai envoyé la lettre hier. – Je l'ai envoyée hier**.

- There is no agreement when the direct object comes after the verb.

- The past participle of an **être** verb agrees with the subject in gender and number: **Elle est allée au théâtre. – Elles sont allées au théâtre.**

Write the appropriate form of the following AVOIR verb participles.

a. Elles ont .... (lire) tous les livres.

b. Elles les ont tous .... (lire).

c. Nous avons .... (copier) toutes les pages.

d. Nous les avons toutes ....(copier).

e. Elle n'a pas .... (pleurer) longtemps.

6 Write the appropriate form of the following ÊTRE verb participles.

a. Elle est .... **(aller)** en ville avec Sonia.

b. Clarèle et moi sommes .... **(rentrer)** à midi.

c. Éléanore et Audrey sont .... **(partir)** après le film.

d. Alain n'est pas .... **(arriver)**.

e. Jean-Luc et Jérôme sont .... **(venir)** à 18 heures.

Agreement with reflexive verbs

- The past participle of a reflexive verb follows the same rules as the past participle of an **avoir** verb.
- If the reflexive pronoun is an indirect object, there is no agreement:

Elle	s'	est	lavée.
subject	reflexive pronoun	être	past participle
Elle	**s'**	**est**	**lavé les mains.**
subject	+ reflexive pronoun/ indirect object	+ être	+ direct object

7 Choose from the list below to fill in the blanks.

a. Ils se sont encore .... !

b. Elles se sont .... leurs adresses.

c. Elle s'est .... le doigt.

d. Elles se sont .... devant la télé.

e. Ils se sont .... pendant de longues minutes.

coupé

regardés

disputés

endormies

échangé

The Perfect Tense (Le passé composé)

- The perfect tense is used to describe completed actions or events which occurred once or several times in the past but not regularly and that are completely finished.

- It is also used to talk about the weather at a specific time in the past (**Il a plu vendredi dernier.**). The perfect tense is formed with either **avoir** or **être + past participle.**

Verbs that take être in the perfect tense

- To form the perfect tense with être, you need the present tense of **être** + the past participle of the verb.

- Remember that when you form the perfect tense with **être**, the past participle agrees with the subject of the verb.

- Only a limited number of verbs take être as an auxiliary in the perfect tense. A fun way to memorise them is to remember them as the **MRS VANDERTRAMP** verbs!

> **M**onter (monté) – **R**etourner (retourné) –
> **S**ortir (sorti) – **V**enir (venu) – **A**rriver (arrivé) –
> **N**aître (né) – **D**escendre (descendu) – **E**ntrer (entré) –
> **R**ester (resté) – **T**omber (tombé) – **R**entrer (rentré) –
> **A**ller (allé) – **M**ourir (mort) – **P**artir (parti)

8 **Match the subject with its auxiliary and verb.**

1. J'
2. Nous
3. Tu
4. Elles
5. Vous
6. Ils

a. avons vu ta sœur ce matin.
b. ont rangé leur chambre.
c. ai gagné la course !
d. êtes restés au parc toute la journée ?
e. es rentrée à quelle heure ?
f. sont allées au marché ce matin.

Underline the correct form of the past participle.

a. Nous avons **regardé / regardés / regardées** la télévision toute la nuit !

b. Elles sont **entré / entrés / entrées** par la porte de secours.

c. J'ai **mis / mise / mises** la voiture dans le garage.

d. Tu as **vu / vus / vues** l'éclipse hier soir ?

e. Samuel et Laurence ont **écouté / écoutés / écoutées** la radio pendant deux heures !

f. Nous avons **pris / prise / prises** un taxi pour rentrer.

 Turn the infinitives into the perfect tense (with <u>elles</u>) and find the correct chronological order.

a. rester deux heures au restaurant.

b. arriver à la gare à six heures.

c. rentrer à l'hôtel se coucher.

d. déposer leurs bagages dans la chambre.

e. téléphoner à l'hôtel pour réserver une chambre.

f. demander au concierge l'adresse d'un bon restaurant.

1. Elles sont arrivées à la gare à six heures.

a.

2. ~~Elles arrivé a~~

3. ....

4. ....

5. ....

6. ....

Congratulations! You have completed chapter 9! It is now time to add up the icons and write the results on page 128 for your final assessment.

Around the Present Tense

The Present Tense (*Le présent*)

- The present tense is used to talk about an action or state of being in the present, about habitual actions, a general truth, the near future, or to talk about an action or state that happened in the past but which is still happening in the present.

- Most verbs form their present tense by adding regular endings at the end of their stem (infinitive form without ending).

- As we have seen previously, there are three main verb groups: the 1st group with infinitive ending in **-er**; the 2nd group ending in **-ir**; the 3rd group ending in **-re** or **-oir** (irregular verbs).

Regular Verbs ending in -ER

J'	aim<u>e</u>
Tu	aim<u>es</u>
Il/Elle	aim<u>e</u>
Nous	aim<u>ons</u>
Vous	aim<u>ez</u>
Ils/Elles	aim<u>ent</u>

1 Underline the right subject pronoun.

a. **Je / Tu / Nous** marches vite.

b. **Tu / Nous / Elles** chantent sous la pluie.

c. **Je / Il / Vous** porte des chaussures.

d. **Elle / Nous / Ils** aidons les sans-abris.

e. **Tu / Nous / Vous** dansez très bien !

f. **Je / Tu / Elle** pense trop !

2 Underline the correct form of the verb.

a. Les touristes **visites / visitent** le musée.

b. Tu **portes / portons** une jolie jupe.

c. Nous **aimons / aiment** la musique classique.

d. À quelle heure **arrive / arrivez** -vous ?

e. Il **chante / chantes** très bien.

3 Conjugate the following verbs in the present tense.

a. Je .... (travailler) dans l'informatique.

b. Tu .... (visiter) ce musée souvent ?

c. Il .... (débuter) le travail à 10 heures.

d. Nous .... (dessiner) ce château régulièrement.

e. Vous ne .... (monter) pas les escaliers ?

f. Elles .... (parler) trop vite !

Irregular -ER verbs

The irregularity can occur within the stem of the verb or the conjugated verb may have a completely different form.

- **Spelling changes**
  - Verbs ending in **-cer** add a cedilla to the **nous** form: **Nous remplaçons les ampoules**.
  - Verbs ending in **-ger** add an **-e** to the **nous** form: **nous rangeons notre chambre**.

- **The 1-2-3-6 verbs**
  The spelling of those verb stems only change in those persons (**je/tu/il/elle/ils/elles**):
  - Verbs like **acheter: e > è = j'achète**
  - Verbs like **appeler: l > ll = elle appelle**
  - Verbs like **espérer: é > è = elles espèrent**
  - Verbs like **nettoyer: y > i = tu nettoies**

- **Note**: **Aller** (*to go*) is the only real irregular **–er** verb in French.

4 Underline the correct form of the verb.

a. Nous **achètons / achetons** des pizzas tous les samedis.

b. Qui **appellent / appelent** -ils ?

c. Il **jette / jète** ses vieilles chaussures.

d. Vous **espérez / espèrez** encore voir Brad Pitt !

e. Nous **envoieons / envoyons** la lettre.

5 Conjugate the following irregular verbs following the above rules.

a. Nous ....
(commencer) la réunion à 10 heures.

b. Je ....
(préférer) le pain complet.

c. Nous ....
(manger) au restaurant ce midi.

d. Tu te ....
(rappeler) le dernier livre que tu as lu ?

e. Elle lui ....
(envoyer) une lettre chaque semaine.

Regular Verbs ending in -IR

Je	fin**is**
Tu	fin**is**
Il/Elle	fin**it**
Nous	fin**issons**
Vous	fin**issez**
Ils/Elles	fin**issent**

6 Conjugate the following verbs in the present tense.

a. Tu .... (**choisir**) d'étudier l'anglais ?

b. Nous .... (**réussir**) toujours les examens d'histoire.

c. Elle .... (**maigrir**) à vue d'œil !

d. Jacques .... (**punir**) souvent son fils.

e. Vous ne .... (**réfléchir**) pas assez !

7 Underline the right form of the verb.

a. Je **choisi / choisis** toujours la mauvaise caisse au supermarché !

b. Nous **finons / finissons** souvent avant le reste de la classe.

c. Vous **bâtez / bâtissez** une nouvelle maison ?

d. Ils **réussent / réussissent** toujours à éviter de faire la vaisselle !

e. Tu **remplis / remplit** trop mon verre !

Regular Verbs ending in -RE	
Je	vend<u>s</u>
Tu	vend<u>s</u>
Il/Elle	vend
Nous	vend<u>ons</u>
Vous	vend<u>ez</u>
Ils/Elles	vend<u>ent</u>

8 Conjugate the following regular -RE verbs.

a. Tu .... (**descendre**) au prochain arrêt ?

b. Vous .... (**perdre**) toujours de l'argent au casino !

c. Sophie et Marc .... (**vendre**) de très jolies fleurs dans leur magasin.

d. Nous .... (**défendre**) souvent notre sœur.

e. Ils n'.................. (**entendre**) pas la cloche de l'église !

Irregular -RE verbs

- There are five irregular **-RE** verb patterns in French:

Prendre *(to take)*: je prends, tu prends, il/elle prend-, nous prenons, vous prenez, ils/elles prennent (drop the **d** in all plural forms and double the **n** in the 3rd plural).

Battre *(to beat)*: je bats, tu bats, il/elle bat-, nous battons, vous battez, ils/elles battent (drop the final **t** in the singular forms).

Mettre *(to put)*: je mets, tu mets, il/elle met-, nous mettons, vous mettez, ils/elles mettent (like *battre* but conjugate differently in the simple past, past participle and imperfect subjunctive).

Rompre *(to break)*: je romps, tu romps, il/elle rompt, nous rompons, vous rompez, ils/elles rompent (3rd person singular adds a **-t**).

- Verbs in **-AINDRE** (**craindre**) and **-EINDRE** (**peindre**): je crains, tu crains, il/elle craint, nous craignons, vous craignez, ils/elles craignent (drop the **-d** in all forms and add a **-g** in front of the **-n** in plural forms).

- All other irregular **-RE** verbs must be memorized separately. Here are a few:

Some common irregular verbs:

Boire *(to drink)*: je bois, tu bois, il/elle boit, nous buvons, vous buvez, ils/elles boivent.

Connaître *(to know)*: je connais, tu connais, il/elle connaît, nous connaissons, vous connaissez, ils/elles connaissent.

Courir *(to run)*: je cours, tu cours, il/elle court, nous courons, vous courez, ils/elles courent.

Croire *(to believe)*: je crois, tu crois, il/elle croit, nous croyons, vous croyez, ils/elles croient.

Devoir *(to have to)*: je dois, tu dois, il/elle doit, nous devons, vous devez, ils/elles doivent.

Dire *(to say)*: je dis, tu dis, il/elle dit, nous disons, vous dites, ils/elles disent.

Faire *(to do)*: je fais, tu fais, il/elle fait, nous faisons, vous faites, ils/elles font.

Falloir *(to be necessary)*: il faut.

Lire *(to read)*: je lis, tu lis, il/elle lit, nous lisons, vous lisez, ils/elles lisent.

Pouvoir *(to be able to)*: je peux, tu peux, il/elle peut, nous pouvons, vous pouvez, ils/elles peuvent.

Savoir *(to know)*: je sais, tu sais, il/elle sait, nous savons, vous savez, ils/elles savent.

Tenir *(to hold)*: je tiens, tu tiens, il/elle tient, nous tenons, vous tenez, ils/elles tiennent.

Venir *(to come)*: je viens, tu viens, il/elle vient, nous venons, vous venez, ils/elles viennent.

Voir *(to see)*: je vois, tu vois, il/elle voit, nous voyons, vous voyez, ils/elles voient.

Vouloir *(to want)*: je veux, tu veux, il/elle veut, nous voulons, vous voulez, ils/elles veulent.

Choose the right verb from the suitcase.

a. Où .... -tu les sacs de voyage ?

b. ....-vous à quelle heure part le train ?

c. Nous .... voyager en avion cette fois-ci.

d. ....-tu porter cette valise, s'il te plaît ?

e. Nous .... aller au terminal 1 ou au terminal 2 ?

f. Je ne .... pas notre porte de départ !

Reflexive Verbs (*Les verbes pronominaux*)

- Remember to change the reflexive pronoun! It agrees with the subject!

- **Note:** in front of a vowel or a silent **h**, **me**, **te** and **se** become **m'**, **t'** and **s'**!

Underline the right pronoun (action done to the same person).

a. Je **me / te / se** douche tous les matins.

b. Elle **me / te / se** brosse les dents deux fois par jour.

c. Nous **nous / vous / se** lavons les mains constamment !

d. Vous **nous / vous / se** rongez encore les ongles !

e. Ils **nous / vous / s'** habillent à 7h15 tous les jours.

The Imperative (*L'impératif*)

- The imperative is used to formulate a command or a request. It is formed by dropping the subject and using the present tense.

- The imperative has three forms which correspond to the **tu**, **nous** and **vous** forms of the present tense.

Tu *form*	**Prends le parapluie**	*Take the umbrella*
Nous *form*	**Prenons le parapluie**	*Let's take the umbrella*
Vous *form*	**Prenez le parapluie**	*Take the umbrella*

- **Note**: also, you must drop the final **-s** in the second person singular of an **-er** verb: **Chante/Ne chante pas!**

- They are of course some exceptions where the present subjunctive is used.

Avoir	Être	Vouloir
Aie	Sois	*(No form)*
Ayons	Soyons	*(No form)*
Ayez	Soyez	Veuillez

11 **Conjugate the following verbs in brackets into the imperative form.**
Eg.: (écrire/tu) sur le cahier. → Écris sur le cahier.

a. .... (écouter/tu) le professeur !

b. Ne .... (regarder/vous) pas par la fenêtre,

mais .... (lire/vous) votre livre !

c. .... (arrêter/tu) de parler avec ton voisin !

d. .... (rendre/nous) nos copies. Le test est terminé.

e. .... (prendre/vous) vos livres

et .... (ouvrir)-les à la page 47.

The Imperative with Object Pronouns

In affirmative commands, the object pronouns come after the verbs and are linked to the verb with a hyphen: **Range-les ! Vendez-la !**

12 **Turn the verb into the imperative and add the appropriate pronoun.**
Eg.: Tu vois le titre? (souligner) → Souligne-le.

a. Tu vois le poème ? .... (apprendre).

b. Vous voyez les livres ? .... (ranger).

c. Tu vois la raquette de tennis ? .... (prendre).

d. Nous voyons les ordinateurs. .... (éteindre).

e. Vous voyez le poster ? .... (accrocher).

Congratulations! You have completed chapter 10! It is now time to add up the icons and write the results on page 128 for your final assessment.

Around the Future Tense

The Future Tense (*Le futur*)

- The future tense is used to talk about an action or a state of being that will occur in the future.

- Now for the good news! All verbs, whether they are regular or irregular take the same endings in the future tense. **-ER** and **-IR** verbs add these endings to their infinitive form and **-RE** verbs first drop the **-e** from the infinitive and THEN add the endings.

	AIMER	FINIR	VENDRE
Je/J'	aimer**ai**	finir**ai**	vendr**ai**
Tu	aimer**as**	finir**as**	vendr**as**
Il/Elle	aimer**a**	finir**a**	vendr**a**
Nous	aimer**ons**	finir**ons**	vendr**ons**
Vous	aimer**ez**	finir**ez**	vendr**ez**
Ils/Elles	aimer**ont**	finir**ont**	vendr**ont**

I Fill in the sentences using the adequate conjugated verb in the beach bag. • •

a. Demain, quand le réveil sonnera, je .... mon maillot de bain.

b. Nous .... au restaurant pour prendre notre petit déjeuner.

c. Comme tous les matins, le serveur nous .... notre cappuccino.

d. Tu .... une salade de fruits frais.

e. Nous nous .... dans l'océan turquoise.

baignerons *servira* *descendrons* *mangeras* *mettrai*

Conjugate the following verbs in the future tense.

a. Nous .... (danser) toute la nuit !

b. Vous .... (choisir) comme vin, messieurs dames ?

c. .... (prendre)-tu de l'eau ?

d. Elles .... (chanter) longtemps à la soirée karaoké.

e. Il .... (rentrer) tard, c'est sûr !

Irregular Verbs in the Future

Some verbs do not use their infinitive form as the stem. Here is an alphabetical list of some of them:

Aller *(to go)*: j'irai, tu iras, il/elle ira, nous irons, vous irez, ils/elles iront.

Avoir *(to have)*: j'aurai, tu auras, il/elle aura, nous aurons, vous aurez, ils/elles auront.

Courir *(to run)*: je courrai, tu courras, il/elle courra, nous courrons, vous courrez, ils/elles courront.

Devoir *(to have to)*: je devrai, tu devras, il/elle devra, nous devrons, vous devrez, ils/elles devront.

Envoyer *(to send)*: j'enverrai, tu enverras, il/elle enverra, nous enverrons, vous enverrez, ils/elles enverront.

Être *(to be)*: je serai, tu seras, il/elle sera, nous serons, vous serez, ils/elles seront.

Faire *(to do)*: je ferai, tu feras, il/elle fera, nous ferons, vous ferez, ils/elles feront.

Mourir *(to die)*: je mourrai, tu mourras, il/elle mourra, nous mourrons, vous mourrez, ils/elles mourront.

Pouvoir *(to be able to)*: je pourrai, tu pourras, il/elle pourra, nous pourrons, vous pourrez, ils/elles pourront.

Savoir *(to know)*: je saurai, tu sauras, il/elle saura, nous saurons, vous saurez, ils/elles sauront.

Tenir *(to hold)*: je tiendrai, tu tiendras, il/elle tiendra, nous tiendrons, vous tiendrez, ils/elles tiendront.

Venir *(to come)*: je viendrai, tu viendras, il/elle viendra, nous viendrons, vous viendrez, ils/elles viendront.

Voir *(to see)*: je verrai, tu verras, il/elle verra, nous verrons, vous verrez, ils/elles verront.

Vouloir *(to want)*: je voudrai, tu voudras, il/elle voudra, nous voudrons, vous voudrez, ils/elles voudront.

3 Read the list of irregular verbs above, cover it and tick the right answers below.

1. Ta lettre est géniale. L' .... -tu à Stéphanie ?
a. ☐ envoya   **b.** ☐ enverra   **c.** ☐ enverras

2. On s'est bien amusées aujourd'hui ! Que ....-nous demain ?
a. ☐ faisions   **b.** ☐ ferons   **c.** ☐ ferrons

3. Cet hôtel est fantastique ! .... -vous à nouveau l'année prochaine ?
a. ☐ Viendrez   **b.** ☐ Viendriez   **c.** ☐ Veniez

4. Le trajet est facile. .... -vous retrouver la route ?
a. ☐ saurai   **b.** ☐ saurez   **c.** ☐ sauriez

5. Quelle journée bien remplie ! Où .... -nous après le restaurant ?
a. ☐ allions   **b.** ☐ allons   **c.** ☐ irons

4 Conjugate the following verbs in the future tense.

a. Demain à la même heure, je .... (être) à la plage !

b. Sandrine, ... (avoir)-tu ton téléphone portable avec toi au restaurant ?

c. Vous .... (voir) ! La piscine de l'hôtel est formidable !

d. .... (pouvoir)-nous faire garder notre petite fille ?

e. Nos filles .... (aller) en excursion la semaine prochaine !

5 Underline the 10 verbs conjugated in the future tense in the following text.

« Marie est très heureuse. Demain, Charles arrivera par le train, un bouquet à la main, prêt à l'épouser. Ils se regarderont et à cet instant précis, se reconnaîtront, pour la vie. Pour le meilleur, et pour le pire. Ils voyageront autour du monde, visiteront tous ces pays dont ils ont parlé sans se lasser. Ils pourront parler sans interruption. Qui sait ? Ils se marieront ; auront des enfants, peut-être. Et vivront dans la paix, sans cette guerre qui a ravagé leur pays. Enfin. Le bonheur. Qui pourrait les en empêcher ? Ils seront ensemble, unis, contre tous. »

The Present Tense for Future

• To express the future, you can simply, like in English, use the present tense: **Demain, je mange au restaurant.** (I am eating at the restaurant tomorrow.)

• **Aller (Present Tense) + Infinitive**
Instead of using the future tense of a verb, you can use the verb **aller** (*to go*) in the present tense followed by the verb in the infinitive form in order to indicate that something is going to happen: **Je vais partir en vacances demain.** (*I am going to go on holidays tomorrow.*); **Il va observer les étoiles ce soir.** (*He is going to stargaze tonight.*)

6 Do you remember how to conjugate ALLER in the present? Let's see!
Fill in the table below!

a. Je ....

b. Tu ....

c. Il/Elle ....

d. Nous ....

e. Vous ....

f. Ils/Elles ....

7 Underline the correct form of ALLER in the following sentences in the future with ALLER (present tense) + Infinitive.

a. Nous allions / **allons** / irons voir le nouveau film de Jean Dujardin demain !

b. Allez / Alliez / **Irez**-vous assister au spectacle ?

c. Je ne allez / irai / **vais** pas manger chez Chloé demain midi.

d. Il **va** / allait / irait encore manger du chocolat en cachette !

e. Quand **vas** / iras / allé -tu aller poster les cartes de Noël ?

8 Turn the following verbs into the future with ALLER (present tense) + Infinitive.

a. Dépêchez-vous ! Le spectacle ....
(aller + commencer) !

b. Ta voiture est en panne ? Pas de problème !
Je .... te ....
(aller + conduire) au garage.

c. Le ciel se couvre : je pense qu'il ....
(aller + pleuvoir).

d. Les Lagrange ....
(aller + visiter) le Vietnam au mois d'août.

e. .... -vous ....
(aller + partir) en vacances cette année ?

Aller (Present Tense) + Infinitive and the Negative Form

- **Ne** is placed before **Aller** and **Pas** after:
Elle ne va pas aller au cinéma ce soir.

- The same rule applies with a reflexive verb: **Il ne va pas se lever à huit heures demain matin**.

9 Turn the following statements into the negative form.

a. Je vais suivre des cours à l'université.

➜ ....

b. Julie va passer son permis de conduire la semaine prochaine.

➜ ....

c. Elles vont se promener en ville cet après-midi.

➜ ....

d. Allez-vous rentrer à dix heures ce soir ?

➜ .... ?

e. Tu vas rester à la maison demain ?

➜ .... ?

Future tense after specific clauses

When the present is used in English, the future tense is used after **aussitôt que** and **dès que** (*as soon as*), **quand** and **lorsque** (*when*), **tant que** (*as long as*), **pendant que**, **tandis que** (*while*): **Je dormirai lorsqu'il arrivera.**

10 Conjugate the following verbs in the future tense.

a. Je
....
(partir) quand Alexandre
....
(arriver).

b. Dorian
....
(aller + aller) chez son frère demain après-midi.

c. Élise
....
(être) déçue lorsqu'elle
....
(apprendre) que Corentin ne vient pas.

d. Nous
....
(venir) tous en vacances avec vous l'année prochaine ! Plus on est de fous, plus on rit !

e. Que
....
(faire)-tu demain à cette heure-ci ?

Congratulations! You have completed chapter 11! It is now time to add up the icons and write the results on page 128 for your final assessment.

12

Around the Past Tense

The Imperfect Tense (*L'imparfait*)

- The Imperfect tense is used to describe things that used to happen regularly in the past: **Quand j'étais petite, j'allais chez mon grand-père tous les mercredis.** (*When I was little, I used to go to my grandfather's every Wednesday.*)

- It is also used to tell how something was like in the past: **Il y avait beaucoup de monde au marché.** (*There were a lot of people at the market.*)

- Additionally, the Imperfect tense is used to describe physical and emotional states such as time, weather, age or feelings: **Il faisait beau lorsque nous étions en vacances.** (*It was sunny when we were on holidays.*)

- It is formed by taking the « **nous** » form of the present tense, dropping the **-ons** ending and adding the following endings: **-ais, -ais, -ait, -ions, -iez, -aient**.

- **Note:** irregular verbs follow the same rules than regular verbs.

- **Remember:** the endings for the imperfect tense are always the same!

	Present	Imperfect
Je	*finis*	**finissais**
Tu	*finis*	**finissais**
Il/Elle	*finit*	**finissait**
Nous	**finissons**	**finissions**
Vous	*finissez*	**finissiez**
Ils/Elles	*finissent*	**finissaient**

	Present	Imperfect
Je	*fais*	**faisais**
Tu	*fais*	**faisais**
Il/Elle	*fait*	**faisait**
Nous	**faisons**	**faisions**
Vous	*faites*	**faisiez**
Ils/Elles	*fontt*	**faisaient**

1 Turn the following infinitives into the present form of NOUS, then into the imperfect form of NOUS.

Eg.: Venir = Nous venons → Nous venions.

a. Partir = Nous .... → Je ....

b. Aimer = Nous .... → Ils ....

c. Croire = Nous .... → Tu ....

d. Prendre = Nous .... → Vous ....

e. Faire = Nous .... → Elle ....

2 Pick the appropriate verb for each sentence.
Beware, there is one too many!

a. Il .... nuit lorsque l'avion a atterri.

b. Nous .... à la plage tous les matins ! Quelles vacances !

c. ....-vous nous voir avant de partir ?

d. Je .... très fatigué.

e. Vous .... tous ensemble ? Vous ....
être à l'étroit !

me sentais

habitiez

allions

deviez   **vouliez**

cuisinait   **faisait**

3 Turn the infinitives between brackets into imperfect forms.

a. Je .... (savoir) que vous .... (être) en France !

b. Il .... (penser) que tu .... (avoir) deux chats !

c. Nous .... (avoir) les cheveux blonds quand nous ....
(être) petits.

d. .... (manger)-tu des pâtes à 3 heures ce matin ?

e. Avant, Caroline .... (appeler) sa sœur tous les soirs.

Perfect or Imperfect?

- The Perfect tense is used for finished actions or events which occurred once or a few times in the past.

- The Imperfect tense is used for actions or events which happened on a regular basis in the past as well as for continuous actions and for descriptions: **J'ai vu ce film l'année dernière.** (Perfect tense)/**Lorsque j'étais jeune, j'allais au cinéma tous les samedis !** (Imperfect tense).

- These two tenses are often used together. The imperfect tense describes what the action was when there was an interruption (Perfect): **Je dormais** (continuous action) **quand tu as téléphoné.** (punctual action).

4 **Perfect or Imperfect? Tick the right column!**

	Passé Composé	Imparfait
a. *Je suis allée au théâtre.*	☐	☐
b. *Il préparait un gâteau au chocolat.*	☐	☐
c. *Nous mangions au restaurant.*	☐	☐
d. *Stéphane a vu un renard dans le pré.*	☐	☐
e. *Marie-Luce dormait à poings fermés.*	☐	☐
f. *Gwendolyne s'est promenée au parc.*	☐	☐
g. *Vous avez regardé le film hier soir ?*	☐	☐
h. *Je lisais mon livre tranquillement.*	☐	☐

DRING !

DRING !

5 **Perfect or Imperfect? Conjugate the verbs in the sentences below.**

a. Je .... (faire) la sieste lorsque la voisine
.... (sonner) à la porte.

b. Lorsqu'il .... (rentrer),
Audrey .... (regarder)
la télévision.

c. Il .... (se rendre) à la banque quand
il l'a .... (rencontrer).

d. Elles .... (être) en vacances et elles
.... (acheter) de très jolis vêtements.

e. Le chat .... (s'apprêter) à bondir lorsque l'oiseau
.... (s'envoler).

6 **Match the sentences together so that they make sense.**

1. Je visitais l'Italie • • **a.** quand il est tombé.

2. Je garais la voiture • • **b.** lorsque tu t'es évanouie ?

3. Elle plantait de la menthe • • **c.** quand la Peugeot m'est rentrée dedans !

4. Passais-tu ton examen • • **d.** lorsque vous vous êtes rencontrés ?

5. Il redescendait la montagne • • **e.** lorsque j'ai rencontré Lorenzo.

6. Vous faisiez du ski • • **f.** quand elle s'est fait piquer par une araignée.

The Present Conditional Tense (*Le conditionnel présent*)

- The Conditional tense is used both in French and in English to express what would happen or what someone would do in certain conditions (after **si**, the verb is in the imperfect tense as seen below). It is also used to express a preference or a wish or to give advice.

- **Note**: **si** becomes **s'** before a vowel or a silent **h**.

Regular Present Conditional
The present conditional is regularly formed by adding the following endings (the same as the Imperfect) to the infinitive form of the verb (for **-RE** verbs, you must drop the **-e** in **-RE**):

Je	regarder<u>ais</u>		Je	choisir<u>ais</u>		Je	vendr<u>ais</u>
Tu	regarder<u>ais</u>		**Tu**	choisir<u>ais</u>		**Tu**	vendr<u>ais</u>
Il/Elle	regarder<u>ait</u>		**Il/Elle**	choisir<u>ait</u>		**Il/Elle**	vendr<u>ait</u>
Nous	regarder<u>ions</u>		**Nous**	choisir<u>ions</u>		**Nous**	vendr<u>ions</u>
Vous	regarder<u>iez</u>		**Vous**	choisir<u>iez</u>		**Vous**	vendr<u>iez</u>
Ils/Elles	regarder<u>aient</u>		**Ils/Elles**	choisir<u>aient</u>		**Ils/Elles**	vendr<u>aient</u>

7 Turn the following infinitives into the conditional tense.

a. Je .... (partir) en vacances demain si je le pouvais !

b. Julian .... (finir) sa toile s'il avait le temps !

c. Avec des « si », on .... (mettre) Paris en bouteille !

d. Martine .... (préférer) prendre le train.

e. Hélène et Simon .... (vendre) leur maison très vite s'ils le voulaient !

8 Conditional and Imperfect: conjugate the verbs between brackets:
Eg.: Si je gagnais (Imperfect) au loto, j'achèterais (Conditional) une nouvelle voiture.

a. Si tu .... (parler) moins, tu .... (finir) plus vite !

b. Vous .... (s'amuser) vraiment si vous .... (venir) en vacances avec nous !

c. Si Luc le lui .... (demander), Aline .... (aimer) beaucoup l'épouser !

d. Nathan .... (être) heureux si Julie lui .... (écrire) une lettre !

Irregular verbs with the Conditional Tense

Avoir and Être
These forms are irregular:

ÊTRE	
Je	serais
Tu	serais
Il/Elle	serait
Nous	serions
Vous	seriez
Ils/Elles	seraient

AVOIR	
J'	aurais
Tu	aurais
Il/Elle	aurait
Nous	aurions
Vous	auriez
Ils/Elles	auraient

Other irregular verbs
The stem is the stem used for the future tense to which you just add the conditional endings:
Aller → j'ir**ais**
Devoir → je devr**ais**
Faire → je fer**ais**
Pouvoir → je pourr**ais**
Savoir → je saur**ais**
Venir → je viendr**ais**
Voir → je verr**ais**
Vouloir → je voudr**ais**

9 Choose the right conditional verb from the box below for each of the sentences.

a. Je .... mieux si tu allumais la lumière !

b. Lucas .... arrêter de courir : il semble essoufflé.

c. Il .... un miracle pour que Béatrice fasse ses devoirs !

d. Il .... la course s'il avait plus confiance en lui.

e. Il fait si chaud, Louise .... tout ce qu'elle a pour une glace !

f. Nous .... déjà arrivés s'il n'y avait pas tant de circulation.

faudrait
gagnerait
verrais
serions
devrait
donnerait

10 Imperfect, Perfect or Conditional? Conjugate the following verbs in the right tense.

a. Je .... (préparer) le dîner lorsque Samuel .... (arriver).

b. Si tu .... (faire) un effort, tu y .... (arriver) !

c. Vous .... (voir) la chenille si vous .... (regarder) de plus près.

d. Nous ne .... (pouvoir) pas comprendre, même si nous .... (essayer).

e. J' .... (écouter) la radio lorsque la nouvelle .... (tomber).

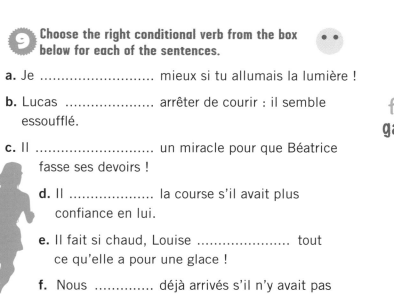

Congratulations! You have completed chapter 12! It is now time to add up the icons and write the results on page 128 for your final assessment.

13
Around Prepositions

What is a Preposition?

- The word "preposition" means "placed in front of". A preposition is a word usually followed by a noun or a pronoun but which can also be linked to a verb: **Il se cache <u>derrière</u> l'arbre**.

- They can be words (**à, dans, sur**) or phrases (**à côté de, en dessous de**).

- **Note:** some prepositions can be used as adverbs: **Il l'a rangé <u>dessous</u>**.

I Underline the prepositions in the following sentences.

a. Anne et Marie se sont cachées sous la table !

b. Vas-tu chez tes parents à Pâques ?

c. Edwige part à Tours avec ses enfants cet après-midi.

d. Guy est allé dans la forêt cueillir des champignons.

e. Elles sont parties pendant une heure.

Preposition with Geographical Names (cities, countries, continents)

Like all French nouns, countries (and places) have a gender. Generally, geographical names ending in an **-e** are feminine, others masculine. There are, as always, exceptions which will need to be learnt!

Towns and countries without articles	à	**Paris** **Barcelone** **Londres**
Masculine countries starting with a consonant	au	**Japon** **Portugal**
Continents, masculine countries starting with a vowel and feminine countries	en	**Europe** **Asie** **Suède** **Afrique**
Plural countries	aux	**États-Unis**

2 Fill in the following blanks using either **À, AU, EN** or **AUX**.

a. Nous allons .... Brésil le mois prochain !

b. Julien voudrait se rendre .... Inde pour les vacances.

c. Nadia vit .... Émirats Arabes Unis.

d. Pablo est-il né .... Espagne ou .... Portugal ?

e. J'adorerais passer Noël .... Fidji !

f. Kate retourne bientôt .... Angleterre.

g. Tu vas .... Lille après-demain ?

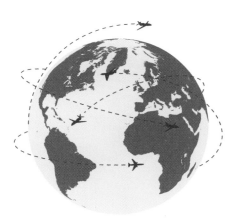

3 Make a full sentence as shown in the example.
Eg: Emilia / Varsovie / Pologne : Emilia vit à Varsovie, en Pologne.

a. Aden / Marrakech / Maroc ....

b. Acha / Yaoundé / Cameroun ....

c. Éléanore / Besançon / France ....

d. Aiko / Tokyo / Japon ....

e. Eeva / Helsinki / Finlande ....

Prepositions and Adverbs of Place
(*Les prépositions et adverbes de lieu*)

- Prepositions of place are used to describe where something is.
- An Adverb is a word or a phrase which modifies the meaning of an adjective, verb or other adverb, expressing manner, place, time or degree: **Elle court vite**.

PRÉPOSITIONS	ADVERBS	English
Dans, en	Dedans	*In, within, into, inside*
Sur, au-dessus de	Dessus, au-dessus	*On, on top (of), over, above*
Sous, en dessous de	Dessous, en dessous	*Under, below*
À côté de	À côté	*Next to, beside*
Devant	Devant	*In front of*
Derrière	Derrière, à l'arrière	*Behind*
Entre	-	*Between*
Parmi	-	*Among*
Contre	Contre	*Against*
Près de	(Tout) Près	*Near*
Loin de	Loin	*Far, A long way from*
En face de	En face	*Opposite*
Au milieu de	Au milieu	*In the middle (of)*
À droite de	À droite	*To the right (of)*
À gauche de	À gauche	*To the left (of)*
En bas de	En bas	*Down from, downstairs*
En haut de	En haut	*Up from, upstairs*
Vers	-	*Near*

 4 Underline the logical preposition in the sentences below according to the context.

a. La balle est tombée **en bas des / au milieu des / en haut des** escaliers.

b. Le poulet est **sous / dans / sur** le frigo.

c. Oh non ! Le chat de la voisine est coincé **en bas de / au milieu de / en haut de** l'arbre ! Il ne pourra jamais redescendre tout seul !

d. Ton cochon d'Inde se cache encore **sous / sur / à côté du** le canapé : il va être difficile de l'attraper !

e. Pourquoi as-tu garé la voiture **devant / dessus / dessous** le garage et non pas dedans ?

5 Using the table above, guess which preposition to use in the sentences below.

a. Le restaurant est-il .... la maison ? Je n'ai pas envie de marcher trop longtemps !

b. La boulangerie se trouve .... la boucherie et le café.

c. Les toilettes sont tout de suite .... escaliers ; vous montez et c'est à votre droite.

d. Je crois que le gâteau est .... la table de la cuisine.

e. Ne te retourne pas ! Il y a une énorme araignée .... toi !

6 Preposition or Adverb of place? Underline the right one!

a. As-tu mis ma chemise **dans / dedans** le sac de voyage ?
– Oui, elle est **dans / dedans** !

b. Regarde ! Hélène est assise **à côté de / à côté** Sébastien !

c. Où est garée la moto ?
– Elle est garée là, **à gauche de / à gauche**.

d. Les clés sont **en dessous de / en dessous** la valise.

e. Oh non ! La maison est encore **loin de / loin** !

« À » and « Chez »

« **Chez** » is used to mean "being at" or "going to" someone's. « **À** » is used with a place.

À + place	**À l'école** **À la piscine** **Au restaurant**
CHEZ + person	**Chez Christophe** **Chez mes parents** **Chez le dentiste**

7 Fill in the following sentences with either À / L' / À LA / AU / AUX / CHEZ.

a. Je suis arrivé en retard .... école ce matin.

b. Vas-tu .... fête du village samedi prochain ?

c. Ils sont allés .... Caroline hier soir.

d. Stéphanie a rendez-vous .... le médecin vendredi matin à 9h30.

e. Elles sont arrivées .... urgences vers minuit.

f. Il vient d'arriver .... bureau.

8 Match the verbs with an adequate complement.

« À » and « De »

- **À** is used to indicate that you are going somewhere: **Je vais à la gare.** (*I am going to the station.*)
- **De** is used to indicate that you are coming from somewhere: **Je viens de la pharmacie.** (*I am coming from the chemist's.*)

à l'école.

de la boîte de nuit !

aux vendanges !

1. Je vais

du cours de guitare.

2. Je sors

du cinéma.

à la pêche avec mon frère !

de l'opéra.

au mariage de Maé et Joris.

Temporal Prepositions (*Les prépositions de temps*)

● **« Dans » and « En »**

Both prepositions mean **"in"** but each is used in a different way. « **Dans** » indicates something that will happen at the end of a certain length of time whereas « **En** » indicates something that happened or will happen within a certain length of time: **Noah arrive <u>dans</u> 10 minutes.** (*Noah arrives <u>in</u> ten minutes. = He will be here <u>in</u> ten minutes.* – **Noah arrive <u>en</u> dix minutes.** (*Noah arrives <u>in</u> ten minutes = It will take him ten minutes to get here.*) It also introduces a date or a time when something happens: **Tom part en vacances <u>en</u> août.** (*Tom is going on holidays <u>in</u> August.*)

● **« Depuis »**

indicates the duration of something that is still going on in the present or that was still going on when something happened in the past: **Il court <u>depuis</u> 20 minutes.** (*he has been running <u>for</u> 20 minutes.*)

● **« Pendant »** (and **« Durant »**)
refer to the duration of an event: **Il a couru <u>pendant</u> 20 minutes.** (*He ran <u>for</u> 20 minutes.*) – **Il courra <u>pendant</u> 20 minutes.** (*He will run <u>for</u> 20 minutes.*)

9 **PENDANT / DEPUIS / DANS / EN ?**

a. Nous allons aller à la plage .... les vacances ! Youpi !

b. Dépêche-toi ! Le train arrive .... une heure !

c. Il habite à Paris .... 2002.

d. La famille Charlet déménage .... septembre.

e. Ils parlent .... des heures quand Jonathan téléphone !

f. Il fait beau .... le début de l'été.

Other Temporal Prepositions

À partir de, dès = *starting from*	**Il y a** = *ago*
Après = *after*	**Il y a … que …** = *for*
Avant = *before*	**Jusqu'à** = *until*
De … à … = *from … to …*	**Pour** = *for*
Entre = *between*	**Vers** = *around, at about*

Fill in the grid below using French temporal prepositions (see their English translation).

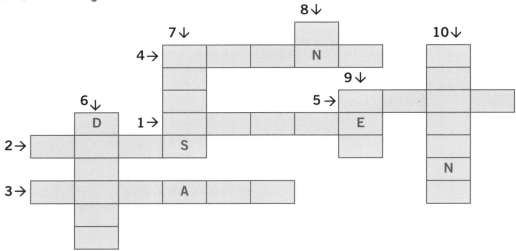

Horizontally
1. Between
2. Near
3. During
4. Before
5. In

Vertically
6. Since
7. After
8. In
9. As soon as
10. During, while

Other common French prepositions. Match the French prepositions with their English translation.

1. au sujet de, à propos de •   • a. *in spite of*

2. avec •   • b. *as for*

3. contre •   • c. *against*

4. malgré •   • d. *with*

5. par •   • e. *except*

6. quant à •   • f. *about*

7. sans •   • g. *according to*

8. sauf •   • h. *by*

9. selon •   • i. *without*

Verbs + Prepositions

De and **À** are the most common French prepositions to follow a verb. Here are a few examples of some constructions with VERB + À/DE + NOUN/PRONOUN/INFINITIVE.

- **VERB + À + NOUN OR PRONOUN**

  Assister à quelque chose = *to attend or be present at*
  Demander à quelqu'un = *to ask someone*
  Faire attention à = *to pay attention to*
  S'intéresser à = *to be interested in*
  Jouer à = *to play*
  Participer à quelque chose = *to participate in something*
  Penser à = *to think of*
  Téléphoner à quelqu'un = *to phone somebody*

- **VERB + À + INFINITIVE**

  Aider à = *to help*
  Apprendre à = *to learn*
  Commencer à = *to begin*
  Demander à = *to ask*
  Réussir à = *to succeed in*

- **VERB + DE + NOUN**

  Changer de = *to change*
  Jouer de = *to play (a musical instrument)*
  Partir de = *to leave*
  Se moquer de = *to make fun of*
  S'occuper de = *to be busy with*
  Se rendre compte de = *to realize*
  Se souvenir de = *to remember*

- **VERB + DE + INFINITIVE**

  Avoir peur de = *to be afraid of*
  Cesser de = *to stop*
  Décider de = *to decide*
  Essayer de = *to try*
  Finir de = *to finish*
  Oublier de = *to forget*

---

12 À / AU / À L' / AUX or DE / DU / DE LA / DES ? Fill in the blanks using the right preposition.

a. Fais attention .... trous ! Ne tombe pas !

b. Julian joue .... la guitare.

c. Ah enfin ! Tu commences .... comprendre cet exercice !

d. Fais demi-tour ! J'ai oublié .... fermer la porte d'entrée !

e. Je me souviens .... jour où la foudre est tombée sur ta maison ! Quelle frayeur !

Congratulations! You have completed chapter 13! It is now time to add up the icons and write the results on page 128 for your final assessment.

14

Around Adverbs

Formation of Adverbs

- An adverb is a word that modifies a verb, an adjective or another adverb.

- Many adverbs (especially adverbs of manner) are formed from another word by adding the suffix **-ment** to the masculine form of the adjectives ending with a vowel (**rapide → rapidement**) or to the feminine form of the adjective if ending with a consonant (**lent → lente → lentement**). There are, of course, some

exceptions to this rule: **bref → brièvement, gentil → gentiment**.

- Adjectives ending in **-ant** change to **-amment** and **-ent** to **-emment** : **courant → couramment** ; **patient → patiemment**.

- A few other adverbs end in **–ément** such as **précisément** or **énormément**.

I Turn the adjectives into adverbs.

a. prudent = ...

b. joli = ...

c. malheureux = ...

d. constant = ...

e. gentil = ...

f. joyeux = ...

g. profond = ...

Place of Adverbs

- In French, adverbs usually come after the verb it modifies. With some exceptions, when the verb is a compound verb, long adverbs come after the past participle: **Julie est rentrée rapidement**.

- Exceptions are **certainement, complètement, probablement** : **Tu as probablement raison.**

- Short adverbs, on the other hand, such as **bien, souvent, mal, beaucoup**, will come before the past participle: **J'ai bien mangé !**

- When the adverb modifies the meaning of an adjective or of another adverb, the adverb comes before it: **Elle est vraiment jolie.**

- In the negative form, adverbs which come after the verb are then placed after **pas**: **Elle dort bien > Elle ne dort pas bien.**

2 Rearrange the words in the right order so as to make a logical sentence:

a. Tellement / Luc / est / fatigué = ...

b. pas / souvent / vais / ne / théâtre / Je / au = ...

c. beaucoup / a / cette / grandi / année / Il = ...

d. Vous / gentils / très / êtes = ...

e. Il / maison / entré / silencieusement / la / dans / est = ...

Adverbs of Manner

- French adverbs of manner mostly end in **-ment** such as **rapidement, sérieusement, lentement, gentiment**.

- You will find below a few adverbs of manner which do not end with the suffix **-ment**.

Adjective	Adverb
Bon → *good*	Bien → *well*
Mauvais → *bad*	Mal → *badly*
Meilleur → *better*	Mieux → *better*

3 Underline the correct word for the context.

a. C'est le **mieux / meilleur** film de l'année !

b. Louis m'a posé la question **gentil / gentiment**.

c. Est-ce un **bon / bien** dessert ?

d. Vous allez **bon / bien** ?

e. Karine va beaucoup **mieux / meilleur** aujourd'hui.

Adverbs of Frequency
(*Les adverbes de fréquence*)

They are usually placed after the verb.

- -	**Jamais**	*Never*
-	**Rarement**	*Rarely*
+	**Quelquefois** **Parfois** **De temps en temps**	*Sometimes* *At times*
+ +	**Souvent** **Généralement**	*Often* *Generally*
+ + +	**Toujours** **Tout le temps**	*Always* *All the time*

4 **Underline the appropriate frequency adverb according to the occupation's description.**

a. Homme d'affaires : Je pars **parfois / souvent** en voyage.

b. Professeur des écoles : Je travaille **quelquefois / toujours** avec des enfants.

c. Fermier : Je travaille **parfois / toujours** avec un ordinateur.

d. Médecin généraliste : Je rencontre **parfois / souvent** des gens.

e. Coiffeur : Je bavarde **rarement / généralement** avec mes clients.

5 **Choose the appropriate adverb from the box to fill in the sentences according to the context.**

a. Le cinéma ? Il déteste ça. Il n'y va ....

b. L'opéra ? C'est tellement cher ! Elle n'y va que très ....

c. La télévision ? Nous adorons ! Nous regardons .... les programmes du soir ensemble !

d. Le théâtre ? Oui, cela lui arrive d'y aller. Pas très .... mais .... il y a un spectacle intéressant.

e. À quelle heure sort-elle du bureau ? Elle en sort .... à 16h30.

rarement

généralement

jamais

quelquefois

toujours

souvent

Adverbs of Time / Temporal adverbs (*Les adverbes de temps*)

Adverbs of time referring to specific days can be placed at the beginning or at the end of the sentence: **Aujourd'hui, je pars en vacances**. They answer the question **Quand ?** (*When?*).

Actuellement = *currently*
Après = *after*
Après-demain = *the day after tomorrow*
Aujourd'hui = *today*

Auparavant = *previously*
Autrefois = *in the past*
Avant = *before*
Avant-hier = *the day before yesterday*
Bientôt = *soon*
Déjà = *already*
Demain = *tomorrow*
Depuis = *since*
Enfin = *finally*
Ensuite = *next*
Hier = *yesterday*

Il y a = *ago*
Jamais = *never*
Longtemps = *a long time*
Maintenant = *now*
Parfois = *sometimes*
Puis = *then*
Rarement = *rarely*
Souvent = *often*
Tard = *late*
Tôt = *early*
Toujours = *always; still*
Tout de suite = *immediately*

6 Find the right missing adverbs of time from the list above. ● ●

a. Mets ton réveil à 5 heures du matin : nous devons nous lever ....

b. Des nuages sont apparus, ... le vent s'est levé.

c. Rex ! Viens .... ! Quelle bêtise as-tu encore faite ?

d. Ne pleure pas Edwige, ta maman va rentrer .... Plus que cinq minutes et elle sera là.

e. J'ai rencontré Carla .... cinq ans et nous ne nous sommes pas quittés depuis !

f. J'adore ce parc ; je viens .... ici.

g. Joshua n'aime pas les carottes. J'en cuisine ....

Adverbs of Place

Adverbs of place are usually placed after the direct object. They answer the question **Où ?** (*Where?*)

À droite = *to the right*
À gauche = *to the left*
À l'intérieur de/dedans = *inside*

Autour = *around*
Dehors = *outside*
Devant = *in front*
En bas = *downstairs*
En haut = *upstairs*
Ici = *here*
Là = *there*
Là-bas = *over there*

Loin = *far*
Nulle part = *nowhere*
Partout = *everywhere*
Près = *near*
Quelque part = *somewhere*

7 Fill in the sentences below using the adverbs of place given in the box.

a. As-tu vu Domino ? – Non, je l'ai cherché ....
mais je ne l'ai trouvé ....

b. Je dois passer l'aspirateur. Allez donc jouer ....
avec le ballon !

c. Finalement, j'ai cherché Domino dehors et
il était .... !

d. Ton revers est incroyable ! Mais où est la balle ?
– Je la vois ! Elle est ...., à côté des arbres !
– Elle est vraiment .... !

e. Victor ? Où es-tu ? Je suis à l'étage et je ne te trouve
pas !
– Mais, je ne suis pas à l'étage, je suis .... !

là-bas partout en bas à l'intérieur dehors loin nulle part

Adverbs of Quantity

Adverbs of quantity explain how much or how many of something there is :

Beaucoup (de) = *A lot (of)*
Assez (de) = *enough*
Peu (de) = *little, few*

Trop (de) = *too much, too many*
Plus (de) = *more*
Un peu (de) = *a little*

• These are often followed by **de** + noun (without article).

peu de   assez de
plus de   beaucoup
de
trop de

8 Fill in the following sentences using one of the adverbs in the sugar box.

a. Beurk, mon café est dégoûtant ! Il y a .... sucre.

b. Arrêtez ! Merci, ça suffira. Il y a ....
lait dans mon café.

c. Le café était calme. Il y avait très ....
gens présents.

d. Désirez-vous autre chose Madame ? – Oui, j'aimerais
.... sucre dans mon café, s'il vous plaît.

e. Je ne sais que choisir ! Il y a ....
gâteaux et ils sont tous appétissants !

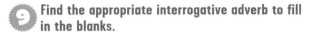

Interrogative Adverbs

Interrogative adverbs are used to ask questions:

Combien (de) = *how much/many*
Comment = *how/what*
Où = *where*
Pourquoi = *why*
Quand = *when*
Quel = *what*
Qui = *who*

9 Find the appropriate interrogative adverb to fill in the blanks.

a. .... est Thomas ? – Il est dans sa chambre.

b. .... es-tu allé à Dijon ? – J'y suis allé en train.

c. .... est avec Florence ? – C'est Laurent, son cousin.

d. .... venez-vous nous voir ? – Nous venons le mois prochain, c'est promis !

e. .... es-tu en colère ? – Oh, cet imbécile m'a pris ma place de parking !

10 Find the appropriate adverbs amongst all the adverbs seen in this lesson to fill in the blanks.

a. On ne risque pas d'avoir un accident : ma grand-mère conduit si .... !

b. Il va .... au travail en vélo. Il adore le grand air !

c. Je pense que cette réponse est correcte : tu as .... raison.

d. Je déteste le poisson ! Je n'en mange ....

e. .... , Jennifer et Océane ne pourront pas venir à ton anniversaire.

f. Julien est .... très généreux.

g. Vous n'avez pas besoin de répéter ; j'ai .... compris.

Congratulations! You have completed chapter 14! It is now time to add up the icons and write the results on page 128 for your final assessment.

Around Verbs

Modal Verbs

Modal verbs are verbs which present a fact as being necessary, possible, desirable and so on.

- **DEVOIR** usually means *to owe/have to/ought to*.

Je	dois
Tu	dois
Il/Elle	doit
Nous	devons
Vous	devez
Ils/Elles	doivent

- **POUVOIR** is used to express ability to and possibility (*can/to be able to*).

Je	peux
Tu	peux
Il/Elle	peut
Nous	pouvons
Vous	pouvez
Ils/Elles	peuvent

- **Note:** when inverted in a question, **je peux** becomes **puis-je**: **Puis-je me laver les mains ?**

- **VOULOIR** means *to want*.

Je	veux
Tu	veux
Il/Elle	veut
Nous	voulons
Vous	voulez
Ils/Elles	veulent

I Fill the blanks by choosing the right verb.

a. .... -vous aller à l'école demain ?

b. Nous ne .... pas manger ou boire ici.

c. .... -je utiliser les toilettes, s'il vous plaît ?

d. Elles .... rentrer à 10 heures.

e. Tu .... venir avec nous au cinéma ?

f. Il .... visiter l'Écosse.

veux

pouvons

doivent

veut

puis

devez

2 Conjugate the following modals in the present tense.

a. Maman, Camille

....

(pouvoir) venir à la maison cet après-midi ?

b. Vous

....

(devoir) ôter vos chaussures avant d'entrer.

c. Je

....

(devoir) étudier pour cet examen !

d. Nous

....

(devoir) faire les courses pour le week-end.

e. Chut ! Elles

....

(pouvoir) nous entendre !

Impersonal Verbs

- **Falloir** is an impersonal verb which is only used in the third person singular (**il faut**) in all of its tenses. It means *to be necessary/to have to.*

- **Valoir (mieux)** means *to be worth/worthwhile/it's better to*: **Il vaut mieux utiliser Skype ! C'est moins cher !** (*It's better to use Skype! It's less expensive!*)

  - **Verbs describing the weather:** expressions describing the weather are impersonal: **Il pleut. Il fait beau**.

- "*There is/are*": **Il y a** is another impersonal expression: **Il y a beaucoup de monde**.

- **Il paraît que/Il semble que/On dirait que : Il paraît que** (*I have heard that/it appears that*) ; **Il semble que** (*It seems that*).

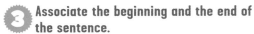

3 Associate the beginning and the end of the sentence.

1. Sortez les skis ! •

2. Je dois trouver mon parapluie ! •

3. Il faut mettre les manteaux ! •

4. Nous pouvons sortir en t-shirt ! •

5. Peux-tu me donner un verre d'eau ? •

• **a.** Il pleut !

• **b.** Il fait beau !

• **c.** Il fait chaud !

• **d.** Il neige !

• **e.** Il fait froid !

4 Translate the following sentences into French.

a. It appears that you were right!

→ ....

b. The weather is beautiful today!

→ ....

c. It's summer! It's very hot.

→ ....

d. It's worthwile having a mobile!

→ ....

e. There are not many people here.

→ ....

When "to be" is not « être »

Some phrases with "be" in English are translated with **Avoir** in French:

To be hungry = **avoir faim**
To be thirsty = **avoir soif**
To be hot = **avoir chaud**
To be cold = **avoir froid**
To be right = **avoir raison**
To be wrong = **avoir tort**
To be lucky = **avoir de la chance**
To be ... years old = **avoir ... ans**

5 Translate the following sentences into English.

a. As-tu froid ? → ....

b. J'ai très faim. → ....

c. Nous avons tort. → ....

d. J'ai 41 ans. → ....

e. Vous avez de la chance. → ....

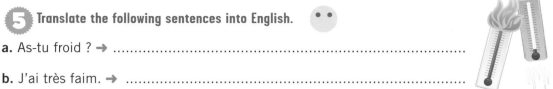

6 Translate the following sentences into French.

a. You are right! It is raining!

→ ....

b. I am really cold! Close the window!

→ ....

c. We are lucky! We won!

→ ....

d. How old is she? – She is 26.

→ ....

e. Are you hungry?

→ ....

Transitive and Intransitive Verbs

• **A Transitive Verb** is a verb that can take a direct object (i.e.: that can answer the question *what?* or *who?*).

Subject	Transitive Verb	Direct Object
J'ai	mangé	un croissant.

• **Note**: when the direct object is a pronoun, it is usually placed in front of the verb.

Subject	Direct Object	Transitive Verb
Je	la	vois.

• **An Intransitive Verb** is a verb that does not take a direct object. It can however take an indirect object (i.e.: it can answer the question *to what? to whom?*). It is often followed by a preposition (**à** for example). Some verbs are intransitive by nature (**pleurer, nager, voyager, etc.**).

Subject	Intransitive Verb	Indirect Object
Nous	parlons	aux voisins.

7 Underline the verbs below and tick whether they are Transitive (T) or Intransitive (I).

Sentence	T	I
a. Nous mangeons une pizza tous les vendredis.	☐	☐
b. Sabine écoute une chanson.	☐	☐
c. Corinne parle à ses amis.	☐	☐
d. Tu réponds à tante Colette ?	☐	☐
e. Je bois du café tous les matins.	☐	☐

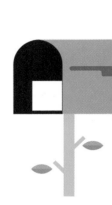

8 Underline the objects below and tick whether they are Direct (D) or Indirect (I):

Sentence	D	I
a. J'ai donné mon livre.	☐	☐
b. Elle téléphone à Alice.	☐	☐
c. Nous écrivons à nos parents.	☐	☐
d. Tu chantes cette chanson.	☐	☐
e. Nous pensons à nos vacances.	☐	☐

Present Participle

- In order to form the present participle, you need to take the nous form of the present indicative tense of a verb, drop the ending **-ons** and add the ending **-ant** (equivalent to the English *-ing*): **Nous regardons → en regardant**.

  Regarder → nous regardons **→** drop **-ons**/add **-ant →** **regardant**
  Vendre → nous vendons **→** drop **-ons**/add **-ant →** **vendant**
  Prendre → nous prenons **→** drop **-ons**/add **-ant →** **prenant**
  Finir → nous finissons **→** drop **-ons**/add **-ant →** **finissant**
  Ranger → nous rangeons **→** drop **-ons**/add **-ant →** **rangeant**
  Faire → nous faisons **→** drop **-ons**/add **-ant →** **faisant**

- There are exceptions to this rule:

  Avoir → ayant
  Être → étant

- The present participle is used essentially in French with the preposition **en** and means "*on*", "*upon*", "*while*", "*by*". It is also sometimes used as an adjective.

9 Turn the following verbs into a present participle.

a. Lancer → ....
b. Aimer → ....
c. Acheter → ....
d. Voir → ....
e. Maigrir → ....
f. Venir → ....
g. S'habiller → ....

Congratulations! You have completed chapter 15! It is now time to add up the icons and write the results on page 128 for your final assessment.

16
Around Linking Words

Linking Words

- Linking words are words which help you connect ideas ad sentences. They are transition words.

- **Conjunctions (Les conjonctions)**
  Conjunctions are words which connect words, phrases, or sentences such as **et, mais, ou, parce que, jusqu'à ce que**.

- **Co-ordinating Conjunctions (Les conjonctions de coordination)**
  Coordinating conjunctions are words which connect words or similar groups of words (nouns to nouns, clause to clause and so on).

- The most common co-ordinating conjunctions are:
  D'ailleurs = *besides*
  Ainsi = *thus*

À savoir = *that is to say*
Au contraire = *on the contrary*
Aussi = *so*
Car = *for*
C'est-à-dire = *that is to say*
C'est pourquoi = *that's why*
Cependant = *however*
Donc = *therefore, consequently*
En effet = *indeed*
Et = *and*
Mais = *but*
Néanmoins = *nevertheless*
Ni ... ni... = *neither*
Or = *however*
Ou = *or*
Pourtant = *however*
Toutefois = *however*
Soit ... soit ... = *either ... or...*

I Underline the co-ordinating conjunctions in the following sentences.

    a. Je suis passé chez toi, mais tu n'étais pas là.

    b. Soit tu viens avec nous, soit tu ne viens pas ; mais, s'il te plaît, décide-toi !

    c. Marion pense cuisiner un bœuf bourguignon ou un navarin.

    d. La voiture est au garage donc je ne pourrai pas venir te voir ce matin. Désolé !

    e. Je ne me sens pas très bien, cependant j'essaierai d'aller en cours.

2 Choose an adequate co-ordinating conjunction from the list above to fill in the blanks below:

car – c'est pourquoi – au contraire – pourtant – à savoir – cependant

a. Julien se pose des questions ....
si la maison sera vendue.

b. Laetitia n'aime pas skier, ...
elle reste au chalet.

c. Florian ne s'énerve jamais, ...
il reste toujours serein.

d. Marine n'aime pas le chocolat, ...
elle a fait un effort et a goûté ton gâteau.

e. Maxime lui fait confiance, ...
il a un doute.

f. Je suis au lit ....
je suis malade.

Subordinating Conjunctions
(*Les conjonctions de subordination*)

- These conjunctions are words which connect a subordinate clause to a main clause.

- A subordinate clause is a clause, typically introduced by a conjunction that forms part of and is dependent on a main clause. The subordinate clause cannot exist by itself, without the main clause: Eg.:

Je l'aime bien	parce qu'elle est très gentille.
I like her	*because she is very kind.*
Main clause	Subordinate clause

- The most common subordinating conjunctions are:

Alors que = *while*
À moins que = *unless*
Afin que = *in order that, so that*
Après que = *after*
Au cas où = *in case that*
Aussitôt que = *as soon as*

Avant que = *before*
Bien que = *although*
Comme = *as, since*
De peur que = *for fear that*
Depuis que = *since*
Dès que = *as soon as*
Jusqu'à ce que = *until*
Lorsque = *when, at the time when*
Maintenant que = *now that*
Parce que = *because*
Pendant que = *while*
Pour que = *in order that*
Pourvu que = *provided that*
Puisque = *since*
Quand = *when*
Que = *that*
Quoi que = *whatever, no matter what*
Quoique = *although*
Sans que = *unless*
Si = *if*
Tandis que = *while, whereas*

3 Underline the subordinating conjunctions in the following sentences.

a. Claudette a pris un parapluie au cas où il pleuve.

b. Bien que Pierre ait peur de l'eau, ils sont allés en vacances au bord de la mer.

c. Comme les enfants n'aiment pas la télévision, j'ai apporté des jeux de société.

d. Je partirai lorsque le film sera fini.

e. Depuis que j'ai 18 ans, je me sens beaucoup plus libre !

4 Match the appropriate subordinating conjunction from the list above to their synonym below.

a. Aussitôt que ....

b. Comme ....

c. Lorsque ....

d. Bien que ....

> **The Subjunctive after Conjunctions**
>
> See Chapter 18 **Around the Present of the Subjunctive**

5 Conjugate the verbs between brackets following the conjunctions.

a. Depuis que je .... (être) en retraite, la vie est belle !

b. Si tu .... (aller) en ville demain, préviens-moi ! J'irai avec toi.

c. Bien que les chiens me .... (faire) peur, je trouve celui-ci très mignon !

d. Quand tu .... (arriver), nous irons voir grand-mère.

e. Quoi que nous .... (dire), ils n'en feront qu'à leur tête.

6 Match the French connectives with their English counterparts.

SEQUENCING

Premièrement / d'abord / tout d'abord •	• *in the first place*
En premier lieu •	• *then*
Deuxièmement •	• *firstly*
Ensuite / puis •	• *secondly*

7 Match the French connectives with their English counterparts.

OFFERING AN ALTERNATIVE

D'un côté... de l'autre •	• *in addition*
D'une part... d'autre part... •	• *moreover*
Ou... Ou... •	• *on the one hand... on the other*
Par ailleurs •	• *on the one hand... on the other*
En outre •	• *either... or*

OPPOSING IDEAS

D'un autre côté •	• *on the other hand*
Par contre •	• *on the other hand*
En revanche •	• *on another hand*
Au contraire •	• *on the contrary*

 8 **Match the French connectives with their English counterparts.**

OFFERING EXAMPLES

Ainsi •	• *for example*
Par exemple •	• *in this way*
Notamment •	• *in particular*
En particulier •	• *particularly*

 9 Match the French connectives with their English counterparts.

CONCLUDE

Finalement / enfin •	• *to conlude*
En conclusion / pour conclure •	• *in short*
En résumé •	• *finally*
En bref •	• *finally*
Pour finir •	• *to summarize / to sum up*

10 Fill in the blanks with the appropriate connective.

a. .... tu pourrais penser à quelques prénoms pour le bébé,
mais ...., tu pourrais attendre qu'il soit né et décider à ce moment-là.

b. Je n'aime pas certains gâteaux : .... , le mille-feuille ou le tiramisu.

c. ...., j'aimerais présenter le sujet de ma dissertation.

d. D'abord on travaille ; ...., on s'amuse !

e. Elle a pris son parapluie ; elle sera .... protégée de la pluie.

Congratulations! You have completed
chapter 16! It is now time to add up
the icons and write the results on
page 128 for your final assessment.

17

Around the Passive

The Passive

- In the active form, the subject performs the action.

- In the passive voice, the subject of the sentence is not the one performing the action. The action actually falls onto the subject.

- The passive voice is formed in the same way as it is in English, i.e. with **être** + past participle + (not always) preposition **par** (*by*).

- **Note:** Some verbs (**aimer, admirer, apprécier, adorer, détester, respecter, accompagner, fatiguer, entourer**, etc.) can be followed by **de: Il est apprécié de ses élèves, je suis accompagné de ma famille.**

- **Être** must agree in number and gender with the subject!

- **Compare**

| Active voice | **Zazie interprète cette chanson.** | *Zazie sings this song.* |
| Passive voice | **Cette chanson est interprétée par Zazie.** | *This song is sung by Zazie.* |

1 Active or Passive voice? Tick the right answer.

	Active	Passive
a. La vaisselle est faite par Joël.	☐	☐
b. Catherine range le garage.	☐	☐
c. Le chat est brossé par Manon.	☐	☐
d. Cette lettre est écrite par mon arrière-grand-mère !	☐	☐
e. Mon père a peint cette toile.	☐	☐

2 Conjugate ÊTRE in the present tense in the following passive sentences.

a. Notre maison .... construite par notre oncle qui est architecte.

b. Les haricots .... plantés par Julien.

c. Nous .... accueillis très chaleureusement par nos amis.

d. Vous .... poursuivis par les petits voisins !

e. Tu .... invitée par Ella.

3 Conjugate ÊTRE in the present tense + past participle in the following passive sentences.

a. Ces tartes ....(être + préparer)
par la classe 3ᵉ D.

b. L'arbre de Noël ....(être + décorer)
par les enfants.

c. Le président français .... (être + accueillir)
par le premier ministre anglais.

d. Les voleurs .... (être + arrêter)
par la police.

e. Les commandes .... (être + prendre)
par la serveuse.

4 Conjugate ÊTRE in the perfect tense + past participle in the following passive sentences.

a. Cette sculpture .... (être + réaliser)
par Auguste Rodin.

b. Ce livre .... (être + écrire)
par Victor Hugo.

c. La voiture .... (être + vendre)
par mon frère.

d. Ces crevettes .... (être + préparer)
par maman.

e. Le ciel .... (être + illuminer)
par la foudre.

Avoiding the Passive

- The passive is used more frequently in English than in French and should be avoided when possible.

- **The Passive with « On »**
If the agent (the "performer") is not expressed or cannot be identified, it can be replaced by « on » + the third person singular of the verb in the active voice: **On m'a dit que tu venais à la fête samedi !**

- **The Passive with « Se »**
When the person by whom the action is performed is not important or relevant, passive constructions using the reflexive pronoun se can sometimes be used: **Les glaces se vendent très bien avec cette chaleur.** (*Ice-creams sell very well in this heat.*)

5 Use the following elements to make a sentence in the active voice using the personal pronoun « ON ».

Eg.: Les clés ont été retrouvées → <u>On</u> a retrouvé les clés.

a. Le bateau a été réparé. → .... le bateau.

b. Le numéro a été changé. → .... le numéro.

c. Le magasin a été ouvert. → .... le magasin.

d. Le vase a été cassé. → .... le vase.

e. La maison a été bâtie. → .... la maison.

6 Conjugate the pronominal verbs with a passive meaning in the following sentences:

a. Comment cela .... (se dire)-il en anglais ?

b. Le vin blanc .... (se servir) très frais.

c. Cela ne .... (se faire) pas. Ce n'est pas poli.

d. Ce plat .... (se manger) chaud et accompagné de haricots blancs.

e. Les toilettes .... (se trouver) au fond du couloir.

7 Turn the sentences in the active voice into sentences in the passive voice (perfect + past participle).

a. Caroline a mangé une pomme. → Une pomme ....

b. Léonard de Vinci a peint la Joconde. → ....

c. L'oiseau a mangé le ver de terre. → ....

d. Daniel a planté les jonquilles. → ....

e. Mathilde a décoré l'appartement. → ....

8 Active or passive voice? Tick the right answer.

	Active	Passive
a. Les cambrioleurs ont été surpris par les policiers.	☐	☐
b. Notre président était respecté de tous.	☐	☐
c. On interdit l'utilisation des téléphones portables dans la salle d'attente.	☐	☐
d. Ce fruit ne se mange pas.	☐	☐
e. Karine est très appréciée de ses collègues.	☐	☐

Where verbs cannot be made passive

- To be turned into the passive voice, verbs must be transitive (with a direct object). A direct object would for example answer to the question *"what"*: **Coralie fait (quoi ?) une tarte. = La tarte a été faite par Coralie** (**faire** = transitive verb).

- Some verbs cannot be made passive in French. Verbs that are followed by **à** + person for instance: **apprendre, conseiller, demander, dire, refuser** are some of those verbs.

- Verbs that take être in the perfect tense cannot be made passive either.

Can these verbs be turned into the passive? Tick YES or NO.

VERB		YES	NO
Demander	*quelque chose à quelqu'un*	☐	☐
Construire	*quelque chose pour quelqu'un*	☐	☐
Aller	*quelque part*	☐	☐
Admirer	*par quelqu'un*	☐	☐
Promettre	*quelque chose à quelqu'un*	☐	☐
Monter	*les escaliers*	☐	☐
Manger	*quelque chose*	☐	☐
Tomber	*par terre*	☐	☐

Congratulations! You have completed chapter 17! It is now time to add up the icons and write the results on page 128 for your final assessment.

18

Around the Present of the Subjunctive

The Present of the Subjunctive

The Subjunctive is not a tense. It is a mood (like the indicative). Like the Indicative, the Subjunctive has got various tenses. The Subjunctive present is the most often used of those tenses.

Forming the Present Tense of the Subjunctive

To form the subjunctive, all you need to do is take the 3rd person plural (ils/elles) of the indicative present tense, drop the ending **-ent** and replace it with the following endings:
-e, -es, -e, -ions, -iez, -ent.

Regarder	
que je regard	**-e**
que tu regard	**-es**
qu'il/elle regard	**-e**
que nous regard	**-ions**
que vous regard	**-iez**
qu'ils regard	**-ent**

Vendre	
que je vend	**-e**
que tu vend	**-es**
qu'il/elle vend	**-e**
que nous vend	**-ions**
que vous vend	**-iez**
qu'ils vend	**-ent**

Finir	
que je finiss	**-e**
que tu finiss	**-es**
qu'il/elle finiss	**-e**
que nous finiss	**-ions**
que vous finiss	**-iez**
qu'ils finiss	**-ent**

I Underline the verb conjugated in the Subjunctive.

a. Il faut que je **réussis / réussisse** mon examen pour entrer à l'université.

b. Je dois prendre ma douche avant que Jean **vienne / vient** me chercher !

c. Pourvu que nous **vendons / vendions** la voiture rapidement !

d. Nous sommes très contents que tu **agrandisses / agrandis** la maison !

e. Il est important que tu **prends / prennes** ton passeport si tu veux vraiment prendre ton avion !

2 Turn the following verbs in the present tense of the Indicative into the present tense of the Subjunctive.

a. Je **mange** du popcorn. ➜ Il est étonnant que je .... du pop-corn.

b. Tu **écoutes** la radio. ➜ Il est important que tu .... la radio.

c. Elle **maigrit** très vite. ➜ Il est surprenant qu'elle .... très vite.

d. Nous **mettons** la table. ➜ Il est utile que nous .... la table.

e. Vous **perdez** souvent vos affaires. ➜ Il est bizarre que vous .... souvent vos affaires.

f. Ils **choisissent** toujours les bonnes cartes. ➜ Il est étonnant qu'ils .... toujours les bonnes cartes.

« Être » and « Avoir »

The subjunctive present form of **Être** and **Avoir**:

ÊTRE		AVOIR	
que je	**sois**	que	**j'aie**
que tu	**sois**	que tu	**aies**
qu'il	**soit**	qu'il	**ait**
que nous	**soyons**	que nous	**ayons**
que vous	**soyez**	que vous	**ayez**
qu'ils	**soient**	qu'ils	**aient**

3 Complete the sentences by conjugating ÊTRE in the present of the Subjunctive.

a. Il faut que tu .... sur ton trente et un pour le mariage de ta sœur !

b. Il est essentiel que nous .... honnêtes durant cet entretien.

c. Je me suis levée en avance pour que vous .... à l'heure.

d. Il est content que je .... premier de ma classe !

e. Il se peut qu'elle .... coupable de quelques délits.

f. Bien qu'ils .... très occupés, ils ont trouvé le temps de venir.

.

4 Complete the sentences by conjugating AVOIR in the present of the Subjunctive.

a. Bien que je n'.................................... pas beaucoup dormi la nuit dernière, je me suis levée aux aurores ce matin.

b. Il faut que tu .... de bons résultats à cet examen.

c. Il est impossible qu'elle .... perdu son portefeuille. Il doit être quelque part !

d. Je suis surpris qu'ils .... décidé de partir à l'étranger.

e. Nous sommes désolées que vous .... mal à la tête. Ce doit être la chaleur !

f. Je crains que nous .... de la pluie demain.

More Irregular Verbs

- **Verbs with an irregular stem and regular endings:**

Aller : (que) j'aille, tu ailles, il/elle aille, nous allions, vous alliez, ils/elles aillent

Faire : (que) je fasse, tu fasses, il/elle fasse, nous fassions, vous fassiez, ils/elles fassent

Pouvoir : (que) je puisse, tu puisses, il/elle puisse, nous puissions, vous puissiez, ils/elles puissent

Savoir : (que) je sache, tu saches, il/elle sache, nous sachions, vous sachiez, ils/elles sachent

Vouloir : (que) je veuille, tu veuilles, il/elle veuille, nous voulions, vous vouliez, ils/elles veuillent

- The rules for **1-2-3-6 verbs** spelling changes are the same than the ones previously explained for the Indicative Present Tense (see **Chapter 10 Around the Present Tense**).

- Some verbs **nous** and **vous** spelling change back to the spelling of the imperfect tense in spite of the **other forms being regular**:

Boire : (que) je boive, tu boives, il/elle boive, **nous buvions, vous buviez**, ils/elles boivent.

Devoir : (que) je doive, tu doives, il/elle doive, **nous devions, vous deviez,** ils/elles doivent

Prendre : (que) je prenne, tu prennes, il/elle prenne, **nous prenions, vous preniez**, ils/elles prennent

Recevoir : (que) je reçoive, tu reçoives, il/elle reçoive, **nous recevions, vous receviez**, ils/elles reçoivent

Tenir : (que) je tienne, tu tiennes, il/elle tienne, **nous tenions, vous teniez**, ils/elles tiennent

Venir : (que) je vienne, tu viennes, il/elle vienne, **nous venions, vous veniez**, ils/elles viennent

5 Find in the box the right verb for each sentence.

a. Nous sommes heureux que vous .... au restaurant avec nous !

b. Il faut que tu .... que je t'ai toujours dit la vérité.

c. Je voudrais que tu .... la vaisselle ce soir.

d. Il est probable que vous .... passer chez nous avant de partir.

e. Il se peut que ton père .... la voiture ce soir.

f. Il faut que tu .... chez le dentiste.

ailles

fasses

veniez

deviez

saches

prenne

6 Conjugate the verbs between brackets in the present of the Subjunctive.

a. Il est étonnant que vous .... (boire) du vin !

b. Je doute qu'ils .... (aller) en Espagne cette année.

c. Il est possible que tu .... (recevoir) une lettre de tante Agathe.

d. Il faut que tu .... (tenir) la corde de ce côté.

e. J'ai peur que vous .... (faire) la queue pendant longtemps.

The Subjunctive after Conjunctions

The subjunctive is used after expressions such as:

À condition que : *on condition that*

Afin que : *in order that*

À moins que : *unless*

Avant que : *before*

Bien que : *although*

Jusqu'à ce que : *until*

Pour que : *so that*

Pourvu que : *provided that*

Quoique : *although*

Sans que : *without*

7 Fill in the blanks using the appropriate conjunction in the box below.

a. Je viendrai samedi, ... je ne vienne dimanche.

b. Je t'ai apporté cette couverture .... tu n'aies pas froid.

c. .... je n'aime pas le poisson, j'ai plutôt apprécié ce dîner.

d. .... il ne vienne pas avec sa femme. Quelle pimbêche !

e. Je continuerai les leçons .... je comprenne toutes les notions.

BIEN QUE   POUR QUE   JUSQU'À CE QUE

À MOINS QUE   POURVU QUE

The Subjunctive after verbs and expressions of wishing and feeling

The subjunctive is used after:
Demander que : *to ask*
Désirer que : *to want*
Espérer que : *to hope that*
Préfèrer que : *to prefer*
Souhaiter que : *to wish*
Vouloir que : *to want*
Avoir peur que : *to fear*
Craindre que : *to fear*

Être content que : *to be pleased that*
Être désolé que : *to be sorry that*
Être heureux que : *to be happy that*
Être surpris que : *to be surprised that*
Regretter que : *to regret that*

8 Conjugate the verbs between brackets.

a. Je souhaiterais que nous .... (gagner) au loto !

b. Il veut que tu .... (venir) avec ton fiancé.

c. J'ai peur que vous .... (finir) tout le gâteau !

d. Je suis surpris que tu .... (vouloir) retourner dans cet hôtel.

e. Je suis désolé que vous n' .... (avoir) pas fait bon voyage.

The Subjunctive after verbs and expressions of possibility and doubt

The subjunctive is used after:

Douter que : to doubt that
Il est douteux que : it is doubtful that
Il est impossible que : it's impossible that
Il est possible que : it's possible that
Il est probable que : it is probable that
Il semble que : it seems that
Il se peut que : it's possible that

9 Pick the right expression of possibility or doubt from the list above according to the context.

a. .... j'aie perdu encore une fois !

b. .... il y ait de l'orage demain. 70 % de probabilité selon le bureau de météorologie.

c. .... nous soyons sélectionnées pour l'équipe nationale ! Cela serait merveilleux !

d. .... ma jambe soit cassée. La radiographie nous en dira plus.

e. .... j'aie la rubéole. Je l'ai eue quand j'étais petit.

The Subjunctive after Impersonal Expressions

Such as:

Il est bizarre que : *it is odd that*

Il est bon que: *it is good that*

C'est dommage que : *it's a pity that*

Il est essentiel que : *it is essential that*

Il est étonnant que : *it is astonishing that*

Il faut que : *it is necessary that*

Il est important que : *it is important that*

Il est nécessaire que : *it is necessary that*

Il est utile que : *it is useful that*

Il vaut mieux que : *it is better that*

Find an appropriate verb within this chapter and according to the context and conjugate it in the present of the subjunctive.

a. Il serait étonnant que je ....(**recevoir**) une lettre d'Olivier. Cela fait des années que je n'ai pas eu de ses nouvelles.

c. Il vaut mieux que nous ....(**aller**) au cinéma demain : ils annoncent de la pluie.

b. C'est dommage que tu ne ....(**boire**) pas de cidre ! C'est tellement bon !

d. Il est bizarre que tu ....(**avoir**) un chien : je croyais que tu étais allergique !

e. Il faut que nous ....(**rendre**) nos livres à la bibliothèque avant samedi.

Other use of the Subjunctive

- It is used after superlatives : **C'est le meilleur livre que j'aie jamais lu !** (*It is the best book that I have ever read!*)

- The subjunctive is also used after indefinite expressions such as **où que** (*wherever*), **qui que** (*whoever*), **quoi que** (*whatever*), **quel que** (*whatever*): **Où que tu sois, je te trouverai !**

- It is also used after verbs of believing and thinking, with verbs such as **croire, penser** when in the negative form: **Je ne pense pas qu'il <u>soit</u> allé au théâtre.**

  Fill in the blanks in the following sentences.

a. C'est le meilleur film que j'..................... jamais vu !

b. .... tu ailles, je penserai à toi.

c. .... tu fasses, je t'aimerai toujours.

d. Je ne crois pas qu'il .... allé en ville.

e. Je ne pense pas qu'il .... de viande.

Congratulations! You have completed chapter 18! It is now time to add up the icons and write the results on page 128 for your final assessment.

19

The Past Historic Tense

The Past Historic (*Le passé simple*)

- The Past Historic though hardly used in conversation is still used in formal written French. It is a literary tense. It is used to describe single and completed actions in the past. It is often used for story-telling, historical writings, in formal, journalistic style. Its use is similar to the use of the perfect (passé composé) but in formal writing.

- Most verbs are regular. The past historic of regular verbs is formed by dropping the infinitive endings and adding the endings below. There are three types of endings:

	Verbs in -er	Most verbs in -ir Some verbs in -re or -oir	Other
Je/J'	*regard* -ai	*fin* -is	*voul* -us
Tu	*regard* -as	*fin* -is	*voul* -us
Il/Elle	*regard* -a	*fin* -it	*voul* -ut
Nous	*regard* -âmes	*fin* -îmes	*voul* -ûmes
Vous	*regard* -âtes	*fin* -îtes	*voul* -ûtes
Ils/Elles	*regard* -èrent	*fin* -irent	*voul* -urent

I Underline all the verbs conjugated in the past historic tense in the following story.

Il était une fois un meunier qui, lorsqu'il mourut, légua tous ses biens à ses trois fils. L'aîné hérita d'un moulin, le cadet d'un âne, et le plus jeune, Paul, d'un chat. « Lorsque je l'aurai mangé, soupira-t-il, il ne me restera plus qu'à mourir de faim ! » Mais le chat l'entendit et prépara un plan : « Ne me mangez pas, Maître. Si vous me laissez en vie, je vous apporterai tout ce que vous désirez. » Paul était sceptique, mais fit ce que le chat lui demandait : « Aussi, si quelqu'un vous le demande, vous vous appelez désormais monsieur le Marquis de Carabas », ajouta le chat. Le chat mit de la nourriture dans son sac et s'allongea sur le sol, comme mort.

2 Conjugate the following verbs between brackets into the historic past.

a. La réunion .... (débuter) à 10 heures.

b. Clément et Zoé .... (arriver) à l'aéroport à l'heure.

c. Nous .... (attendre) pendant des heures. La tension .... (monter).

d. Vous .... (partir). La maison .... (sembler) vide.

e. Je .... (prendre) beaucoup de photos ce jour-là.

« Avoir » and « être »

Avoir (*have*) and **être** (*be*) are both irregular:

AVOIR	ÊTRE
J'eus	Je fus
Tu eus	Tu fus
Il/Elle eut	Il/Elle fut
Nous eûmes	Nous fûmes
Vous eûtes	Vous fûtes
Ils/Elles eurent	Ils/Elles furent

3 Conjugate the following AVOIR verbs.

a. Elles .... soudain très soif.

b. Nous .... l'idée d'aller au cinéma tous ensemble.

c. Lorsqu'elle ouvrit la fenêtre, j'.................... très froid.

d. Il .... une peur bleue lorsque la foudre tomba sur la maison voisine !

e. Vous .... beaucoup de difficultés à organiser ce voyage.

Conjugate the following ÊTRE verbs.

a. Ils .... les premiers soldats américains à Paris.

b. Nous .... très surpris.

c. Louis de Funès .... très célèbre dans les années 1970.

d. Tu .... un des élèves les plus populaires du lycée !

e. Vous .... très heureux de réussir votre examen.

Irregular Verbs

Verbs in **-oir** are irregular. Here is a list of some irregular verbs:

Aller : j'allai, tu allas, il/elle alla, nous allâmes, vous allâtes, ils/elles allèrent

Boire : je bus, tu bus, il/elle but, nous bûmes, vous bûtes, ils/elles burent

Connaître : je connus, tu connus, il/elle connut, nous connûmes, vous connûtes, ils/elles connurent

Courir : je courus, tu courus, il/elle courut, nous courûmes, vous courûtes, ils/elles coururent

Croire : je crus, tu crus, il/elle crut, nous crûmes, vous crûtes, ils/elles crurent

Devoir : je dus, tu dus, il/elle dut, nous dûmes, vous dûtes, ils/elles durent

Dire : je dis, tu dis, il/elle dit, nous dîmes, vous dîtes, ils/elles dirent

Écrire : j'écrivis, tu écrivis, il/elle écrivit, nous écrivîmes, vous écrivîtes, ils/elles écrivirent

Faire : je fis, tu fis, il/elle fit, nous fîmes, vous fîtes, ils/elles firent

Falloir : il fallut

Mettre : je mis, tu mis, il/elle mit, nous mîmes, vous mîtes, ils/elles mirent

Prendre : je pris, tu pris, il/elle prit, nous prîmes, vous prîtes, ils/elles prirent

Savoir : je sus, tu sus, il/elle sut, nous sûmes, vous sûtes, ils/elles surent

Tenir : je tins, tu tins, il/elle tint, nous tînmes, vous tîntes, ils/elles tinrent

Venir : je vins, tu vins, il/elle vint, nous vînmes, vous vîntes, ils/elles vinrent

Voir : je vis, tu vis, il/elle vit, nous vîmes, vous vîtes, ils/elles virent

5 Underline the **IRREGULAR** verbs in the past historic tense in the following story.

Le Petit Poucet dut se lever de bon matin et prit le chemin du ruisseau. Il emplit ses poches de petits cailloux blancs et revint ensuite à la maison. Il alla dans une forêt dense. Le bûcheron se mit à couper du bois et les enfants ramassèrent des brindilles. Lorsque les parents virent que les enfants étaient occupés, ils s'enfuirent rapidement. Le Petit Poucet courut partout pour retrouver ses parents mais dut renoncer, tristement.

6 Conjugate the following irregular verbs in the past historic tense.

a. Elle .... (mettre) sa robe rapidement pour ne pas être en retard !

b. Ils .... (reconnaître) le bandit et lui .... (courir) après.

c. Je .... (savoir) immédiatement que quelque chose lui était arrivé.

d. Nous .... (aller) au restaurant après la cérémonie.

e. Vous .... (devoir) prendre le train plus tard que prévu suite aux intempéries.

Verbs in -ger and -cer

- These verbs are **-ger** verbs (such as **manger**) where **-g** changes to **-ge** and **-cer** verbs (such as **lancer**) where **-c** changes to **-ç** to maintain the soft sound.

- The spelling change occurs at all persons except the third person plural:

Manger = je mangeai, tu mangeas, il/elle mangea, nous mangeâmes, vous mangeâtes, ils/elles mangèrent

Lancer = je lançai, tu lanças, il/elle lança, nous lançâmes, vous lançâtes, ils/elles lancèrent

7 Conjugate the following verbs in the past historic tense:

a. Ils .... (avancer) dans la neige avec difficulté.

b. Nous .... (voyager) pendant deux mois !

c. Il .... (neiger) toute la journée et toute la nuit sans interruption.

d. Vous .... (commencer) la réunion sans Romain, qui était en retard.

e. Martin .... (remplacer) David qui était malade.

f. Vous .... (nager) pendant deux heures : quelles athlètes !

8 Regular and Irregular verbs. Fill in the following Crosswords!

Vertically
1. J' .... (habiller)
2. Nous .... (tenir)
3. Ils .... (finir)
4. Elle .... (remplacer)

Horizontally
5. Il................ (hurler)
6. Nous .... (boire)
7. Il .... (falloir)
8. Elle .... (regarder)
9. Elles .... (placer)

9 La petite poule rousse : pick the right verbs from the henhouse and place them at the right place within the following story:

Il était une fois une petite poule rousse qui .... de chez elle
pour aller en ville. Elle .... la clé dans sa poche mais
sa poche avait un trou et la clé .... par terre.
La petite poule ne le .... pas et .... son chemin.
Maître Renard .... Il n'avait qu'une envie : manger
la poulette ! Lorsqu'il .... la clé sur le sol, il la
.... et .... ouvrir la porte de la maisonnette.

apparut

sortit

vit

aperçut

couru

poursuivit

mit

ramassa

tomba

Congratulations! You have completed chapter 19! It is now time to add up the icons and write the results on page 128 for your final assessment.

1 Funny French phrases and Idioms - write the appropriate article (definite and indefinite) in the following French expressions:

a. J'ai .... cafard. (masc.)
→ *lit. > I have the cockroach. = I feel down.*

b. Tu me casses .... oreilles !
→ *lit. > You are breaking my ears. = The noise you are making is really irritating me.*

c. Il m'a posé .... lapin !
→ *lit. > He put me down a rabbit. = He stood me up.*

d. C'est .... fin .... haricots !
→ *lit. > It is the end of the beans. = It's the last straw.*

e. Arrête de faire .... andouille ! (type of sausage)
→ *lit. > Stop making the sausage. = Stop acting like a fool!*

2 Unscramble the following anagrams in order to find names of occupations and translate them into English.

a. preesfousr = un ....

b. canuhetr = un ....

c. veesudne = une ....

d. méecdin = un ....

e. iégienunr = un ....

f. seuvrer = un ....

g. cceiogrne = un ....

h. blugeonar = un ....

3 Find and underline the odd one out in the following series of words.

a. as – est – avez – ont – ai

b. mangé – choisi – fait – étant – porté

c. te – nous – elles – je – vous

d. Français – Mexique – Australien – Hollandais – Italien

e. bleu – rouge – vert – chat – rose

4 Fill in the "crossadjective" with adjectives using the definitions given.

Vertically
1. Ils sont généreux, prévenants, attentionnés.
2. Contraire de maigre.
3. Il n'arrête pas de parler.
4. Il est beau, mignon.
5. Elle a du chagrin ; elle a envie de pleurer.
6. Il ne rit pas et a l'air grave.
7. Elle est de grande taille.

Horizontally
8. Elles sont réelles, exactes.
9. Contraire de mauvais.
10. Qui peut attendre ; persévérant.
11. Contraire de petit.
12. Il est âgé.
13. Certain ou sécurisé.
14. Il cherche à faire du mal.

							6↓
1↓			4↓ 8→	**V**			
G		9↓	**J**				
	3↓	**B**		**E**			
	B		5↓				
10→ **P**							
2↓							7↓
11→ **G**		12→ **V**					
13→ **S**							
14→ **M**							

5 Sentence jumble — Put the mixed up words together to form a sentence:

a. allé / avec / Quentin / amis / est / cinéma / au / ses :

....

b. l' / grand / faire / Je / un / pense / prochaine / voyage / année :

....

c. une / Ils / pour / anniversaire / organiseront / Marion / fête / d' :

....

d. lorsque / faisais / porte / la / la / as / à / Je / sieste / frappé / tu

....

e. dès / travail / commencera / Eva / retour / le / son

....

6 How well do you remember your regular and irregular conjugations? Fill in the grid below!

Verb	Present	Perfect	Future	Conditional	Imperfect
Regarder	Je regarde	J'	Je regarderai	Je	Je ....
Faire	Tu	Tu	Tu feras	Tu	Tu faisais
Vendre	Il vend	Il	Il	Il vendrait	Il ....
Finir	Nous	Nous avons fini	Nous finirons	Nous	Nous ....
Boire	Vous	Vous	Vous boirez	Vous	Vous buviez
Aller	Elles vont	Elles	Elles	Elles iraient	Elles ....

 7 Time match – Line match the clock and the written time.

Il est une heure trente.
Il est quatre heures et demie.
Il est onze heures moins le quart.
Il est deux heures et quart.
Il est midi.
Il est huit heures moins dix.
Il est trois heures vingt-cinq.

`01:30`
`12:00`
`02:15`

`10:45`
`04:30`
`07:50`
`03:25`

 8 Linking Words Word Search.

Ainsi
Néanmoins
Pourtant
Mais
Aussi
Car
Donc
Quand
Quoique
Lorsque
Comme
Toutefois

R	E	H	A	C	O	M	M	E	P
G	A	T	I	S	S	O	N	L	O
A	B	O	N	N	U	G	M	O	U
Q	Y	N	S	A	C	I	O	R	R
B	U	K	I	U	J	A	V	S	T
G	Q	O	X	D	Q	F	R	Q	A
M	U	S	I	R	O	I	L	U	N
O	A	B	M	Q	C	N	A	E	T
M	N	X	B	E	U	O	C	Q	L
A	D	O	L	G	F	E	R	A	I
I	T	O	U	T	E	F	O	I	S
S	R	D	J	A	U	S	S	I	A
N	E	A	N	M	O	I	N	S	O

9 Build a sentence — make sentences using one segment in each columns.

Eg.: Elles	as compris	au cinéma hier.
a. J'	a été	ma tarte aux pommes ?
b. Il	sommes partis	toute la nuit !
c. Vous	ai rêvé	à 8 heures.
d. Tu	avez aimé	l'exercice de grammaire ?
e. Nous	ont dansé	que je gagnais au loto !

Eg.: Elles ont dansé toute la nuit !

a. ....

b. ....

c. ....

d. ....

e. ....

10 Numbers and their written forms have been mixed up. Can you put them back together?

1. **46** •
2. **99** •
3. **318** •
4. **72** •
5. **502** •
6. **152** •
7. **1008** •
8. **683** •

• **a.** cent cinquante-deux
• **b.** cinq cent deux
• **c.** quarante-six
• **d.** six cent quatre-vingt-trois
• **e.** mille huit
• **f.** trois cent dix-huit
• **g.** soixante-douze
• **h.** quatre-vingt-dix-neuf

Congratulations! You have completed chapter 20! It is now time to add up the icons and write the results on page 128 for your final assessment.

1. Alphabet and Pronunciation

2 **a.** Une mère = a mother – **b.** Peut-être = maybe – **c.** Noël = Christmas – **d.** Une leçon = a lesson – **e.** Le présent = the present – **f.** Tôt = early – **g.** Un garçon = a boy – **h.** Le passé = the past

3 **a.** père – **b.** Noël – **c.** glaçons – **d.** passé – **e.** même

4 **froid** = cold – **porc** = pork – **trois** = three – **vous** = you – **abricot** = apricot – **chez** = at – **mot** = word – **chat** = cat – **salut** = hi – **outil** = tool – **estomac** = stomach – **beaucoup** = a lot – **trop** = too (much / many) – **nerf** = nerve – **deux** = two

5 **Silent Letter :** poule – lourd – froid
Pronounced Letter : Turc – œuf – four – ours – hiver

7

Sentence	Y	N
Un homme	✓	
Les élèves	✓	
Les haricots		✓
Les vieux éléphants	✓	
Le petit ami	✓	
Les yeux	✓	

8

	1	2	3	4	5	6	7	8	9	10
A					M			H		
B	V			B	O	N	J	O	U	R
C	O			E	T			M		A
D	U			A				M		V
E	S	A	L	U	T			E		I
F				C						E
G		F	R	O	I	D		M		
H				U		E	L	E	V	E
I	T	R	O	P				U		R
J								X		E

9 « Mon **père** est **rentré** hier soir du Venezuela pour **fêter Noël** en famille. Il veut des **festivités françaises** ! C'est **génial d'être** enfin ensemble ! C'est l'heure des cadeaux et des escargots ! Nous allons nous **régaler** ! Quelle **fête** cela sera ! »

2. Around Articles and Nouns

1

Nouns	M	F	P
Salon	✓		
Chambre		✓	
Toilettes			✓
Cave		✓	
Grenier	✓		
Cuisine		✓	

2

Masc. Sing.	Fem. Sing.	Masc. Plu.
Un ami	Une amie	**Des amis**
Un Français	**Une Française**	**Des Français**
Un marchand	**Une marchande**	Des marchands
Un marié	**Une mariée**	**Des mariés**
Un avocat	Une avocate	**Des avocats**
Un invité	**Une invitée**	Des invités

3 **a. La** maison est grande ! – **b. Les** filles sont très jolies ! – **c. Les** enfants sont gentils. – **d. L'**eau est trop froide ! – **e. Le** garçon joue au football. – **f. L'**homme est très grand !

4 Le garçon – La chambre – L'araignée – Les chaussures – Le vent

5 **a.** Il y a **un** chat sur le toit. – **b.** As-tu **des** crayons dans ta trousse ? – **c.** Je mange **des** gâteaux tous les jours. – **d.** Il veut **une** guitare pour Noël. – **e.** Nous avons **un** chien.

6 « Garçon, s'il vous plaît ! Je voudrais **une** pizza avec **des** champignons, **du** jambon et **de la** sauce tomate. Je veux **la** pizza rapidement car j'ai très faim ! J'aimerais aussi **de l'**eau ! Merci ! »

7 **a.** Tu **n'**as **pas** de jardin. – **b.** Nous **n'**avons **pas** d'enfants. – **c.** Ils **n'**ont **pas** de gentils parents. – **d.** Je **n'**ai **pas** de maison. – **e.** Elles **n'**ont **pas** d'amis.

8 un avocat = a lawyer – un chanteur = a singer – un professeur = a teacher – un serveur = a waiter – un concierge = a caretaker – un écrivain = a writer – un ingénieur = an engineer

9

Masculine	Feminine
Un vendeur	**Une vendeuse**
Un musicien	Une musicienne
Un acteur	**Une actrice**
Un boulanger	Une boulangère
Un étudiant	Une étudiante
Un maître	**Une maîtresse**
Un paysan	**Une paysanne**
Un secrétaire	Une secrétaire
Un dentiste	**Une dentiste**
Un professeur	**Une professeure/Un professeur**

3. Around Pronouns Part 1

1 **a. Tu** es très grande ! – **b. Elle** a quarante-cinq ans. – **c. Nous** sommes Canadiens. – **d. Elles** adorent les araignées ! – **e. Vous** êtes très élégantes !

2 **a. Elles** sont au Kenya. – **b. Vous** êtes au cinéma ? – **c. Elle** est heureuse. – **d. Nous** sommes à la boulangerie. – **e. Je** suis allergique au pollen.

3 **a.** Il **est** peintre. – **b.** Nous **sommes** étudiants. – **c.** Elles **sont** actrices. – **d.** Vous **êtes** boulangers ? – **e.** Je **suis** traducteur.

4 **a.** J'ai 45 ans. – **b.** Nous **avons** un chien. – **c.** Ils **ont** 3 vélos. – **d.** Tu **as** une moto ? – **e.** Elle **a** 2 maisons.

5 a. Philippe **est** ingénieur. – **b.** Karine **a** un chien et deux hamsters. – **c.** Clémentine **est** très jolie. – **d.** Nicolas **est** gentil. – **e.** Oriane **a** une belle robe.

6 a. Elle **est** courageuse. – **b. Vous** avez une belle voiture ! – **c. Nous** sommes en Australie. – **d. Ils** sont petits. – **e. Je suis** Belge.

7 a. Je **l'**aime ! – **b.** Tu **m'**attends quelques minutes ? – **c.** Elles **nous** ont invités au restaurant. – **d.** Je **vous** ai vus au cinéma. – **e.** Stéphanie **t'**attend depuis une heure.

8 a. le train – **b.** Maéva ou Bruno – **c.** la fourchette – **d.** ses cousins ou ses cousines – **e.** toi et ton amie

9 a. Il **lui** a dit bonjour. – **b.** Je **vous** ai donné une lettre. – **c.** Marie **nous** pose une question. – **d.** Elle **lui** téléphone tous les dimanches. – **e.** Ton père **t'**a répondu.

10

```
                    5
            6  L  A
        3      E
    4  N  O  U  S
    1      O     R
8  7  L  U  I
2  V  O  U  S
   O     I
   U
   S
```

4. Around Adjectives

1

Masc. Sing.	Fem. Sing.	Masc. Plu.	Fem. Plu.
Français	Française	**Français**	Françaises
Mexicain	Mexicaine	Mexicains	Mexicaines
Grand	Grande	Grands	**Grandes**
Gros	Grosse	**Gros**	Grosses
Poli	**Polie**	Polis	Polies
Beau	Belle	Beaux	**Belles**
Bon	**Bonne**	Bons	Bonnes
Vieux	Vieille	Vieux	Vieilles

2 a. Elle est vraiment très **gentille** ! – **b.** Ces chiens sont **méchants**. – **c.** Sois **patient** Sébastien. – **d.** Elles sont vraiment **bavardes** ! – **e.** Oh Marceau, avec un tel sourire, toi, tu es **amoureux** ! – **f.** Ils sont tellement **maladroits** !

3 a. Oh, regarde ! Quel **beau** paysage ! – **b.** J'aime beaucoup cette robe **rouge**. – **c.** C'est une fille **jalouse**. – **d.** Quel **joli** tableau ! – **e.** C'était un **long** voyage.

4 a. Mon ami est **anglais**. – **b.** Cette fille est **coréenne**. – **c.** Ses parents sont **finlandais**. – **d.** Ce groupe de musique est **canadien**. – **e.** Les joueurs de cette équipe sont **chinois**. – **f.** Les chanteuses de cette chorale sont **américaines**.

5

Flags	Masc. Sing.	Fem. Sing.	Masc. Pl.	Fem. Pl.
	Hollandais	Hollandaise	Hollandais	Hollandaises
	Espagnol	Espagnole	Espagnols	Espagnoles
	Italien	Italienne	Italiens	Italiennes
	Suédois	Suédoise	Suédois	Suédoises
	Irlandais	Irlandaise	Irlandais	Irlandaises
	Norvégien	Norvégienne	Norvégiens	Norvégiennes
	Japonais	Japonaise	Japonais	Japonaises
	Mexicain	Mexicaine	Mexicains	Mexicaines
	Brésilien	Brésilienne	Brésiliens	Brésiliennes
	Allemand	Allemande	Allemands	Allemandes

6

Colours	Masc. Sing.	Fem. Sing.	Masc. Pl.	Fem. Pl.
	Violet	Violette	Violets	Violettes
	Vert	Verte	Verts	Vertes
	Bleu	Bleue	Bleus	Bleues
	Orange	Orange	Orange	Orange
	Gris	Grise	Gris	Grises
	Blanc	Blanche	Blancs	Blanches
	Noir	Noire	Noirs	Noires
	Rouge	Rouge	Rouges	Rouges
	Marron	Marron	Marron	Marron
	Rose	Rose	Roses	Roses

7 a. De belles chaussures **bleues**. – **b.** De très jolies fleurs **jaunes**. – **c.** De beaux pulls **marron**. – **d.** Une élégante cravate **noire**. – **e.** Un buisson **vert**.

8 a. J'ai beaucoup aimé **ce** film ! – **b.** Quelle horreur ! **Cette** pomme était pourrie ! **c. Ces** enfants sont très bruyants. – **d.** Peux-tu me passer **ce** plat, s'il te plaît ? – **e. Cet** homme a une cravate rigolote !

9 a. As-tu vu **mon** livre ? Je ne le trouve pas ! – **b. Ses** sœurs sont très grandes ! – **c.** J'adore **leur** chien ! Il est très amusant ! – **d. Son** amie s'appelle Éléanore. – **e. Ton** père est très gentil Anne !

10 a. Il a des cheveux bruns/marron. – **b.** Son père est français. – **c.** Leur chat est blanc. – **d.** Elle s'est lavé les cheveux hier. – **e.** Votre maison est très grande !

5. Around Comparatives and Superlatives

1 **a.** Son chat est **moins rapide que** son chien ! – **b.** Floriane est **aussi jolie que** Martine. – **c.** Ce livre est **plus intéressant que** celui-là. – **e.** Laurent est **moins gentil que** Sylvain. – **f.** Ta maison est **aussi grande que** la mienne.

2 **a.** This table is bigger than that one. – **b.** Alexandre is as sporty as Julien. – **c.** Sophie is less pretty than Karine. – **d.** Julien is as funny as Lily. – **e.** The blue bag is more practical than the black one.

3 **a.** Elles sont plus **bavardes** que nous. – **b.** Marion est aussi **belle** que Sophie. – **c.** Emmanuel est aussi **intelligent** que Claire. – **d.** Louis et Gabriel sont moins **gentils** que Catherine et Jennifer. – **e.** L'arbre de droite est plus **petit** que l'arbre de gauche.

4 **Adjectives:** Gentil – Belle
Adverbs: Rapidement – Mieux – Facilement – Malheureusement

5 **a.** Rare > **Rarement** – **b.** Poli > **Poliment** – **c.** Courageux > **Courageuse** > **Courageusement** – **d.** Prudent > **Prudemment** – **e.** Parfait > **Parfaite** > **Parfaitement**

6 **a.** C'est **la** plus belle maison du quartier. – **b.** Ce sont les garçons **les** plus polis de la classe ! – **c.** Ce sont **les** robes les plus laides du magasin. – **d.** C'est **le** chien le plus méchant du parc. – **e.** C'est **la** fille la plus jolie du village.

7 **a.** Ces fleurs sont les plus **colorées** du jardin. – **b.** Elle est la plus **active** de sa classe. – **c.** Ce bébé est le plus **mignon** que je connaisse. – **d.** Leurs voitures sont les plus **propres** de la rue ! – **e.** Jeanne est la femme la plus **maladroite** !

8 **a.** C'est la maison **la** plus chère du quartier. – **b.** Sophie est la fille **la** moins sportive du groupe. – **c.** Jonathan est le garçon le plus rapide **de** son club. – **d.** Les dattes sont les fruits **les** plus sucrés. – **e.** Joséphine est la plus maligne **de** l'école.

9 **a.** Élisa est **aussi étourdie que** Vanessa. – **b.** C'est **le meilleur** gâteau du menu. – **c.** Ils sont **aussi timides que** leurs parents. – **d.** Audrey est la fille **la plus généreuse** que je connaisse. – **e.** Ce livre est **le pire que** j'aie jamais lu.

6. Around Sentence and Forms

1

	Subject	Verb	Complement
a.	Il	mange	du gâteau.
b.	Nous	avons vu	Charles et Simon.
c.	Vous	chantez	une belle mélodie.
d.	Elle	donne	des bonbons.
e.	Nous	aimons	les films de science-fiction.

2 **a.** Julie a invité ses amis au restaurant. – **b.** Sylvain a acheté une nouvelle voiture. – **c.** Son pull est très joli. – **d.** Christian voyage souvent en train. – **e.** Léon prend son petit déjeuner à 8 heures.

3 **a.** Estelle **n'est plus** malade. – **b.** Martine **n'a ni** chat **ni** chien. – **c.** Stéphanie **n'est pas** méchante. – **d.** Roger **n'a jamais** mangé de calamar. – **e.** Julian **n'a rien** bu hier soir.

4 **a.** Achille **n'aime pas** les fraises. – **b.** Violette **ne joue pas / jamais** au tennis. – **c.** Romain **n'est pas** blond. – **d.** Séverine **n'aime pas** les films d'aventure. – **e.** Olivier **n'est pas** petit.

5 **a.** Est-ce que Ginette aime les poires ? – **b.** Françoise parle-t-elle le chinois ? – **c.** Est-ce que Marine vit en Australie ? – **d.** Peut-il venir me voir ? – **e.** Veut-elle écouter mon CD ?

6 **a.** Est-ce qu'il déteste les chats ? – **b.** Est-ce que tu vas au cinéma ? – **c.** Est-ce que vous regardez la télé ? – **d.** Est-ce qu'ils sont allés en Italie ? – **e.** Est-ce qu'elle aime ma confiture ?

7 **a.** **À quelle heure** son train arrive-t-il à la gare ? – **b.** **Qui** a mangé mon yaourt ? – **c.** **Combien** ce collier coûte-t-il ? – **d.** **Comment** es-tu rentré ? – **e.** **Que** fait-il dans sa chambre ?

8 **a.** Comment vas-tu ? – **b.** Où habite-t-il ? – **c.** Combien de temps le film a-t-il duré ? – **d.** Pourquoi Sophie est-elle rentrée ? – **e.** Qui a cassé le vase ?

9 **a.** Je ne vais jamais au théâtre. – **b.** Qui a pris mon livre ? – **c.** Quand rentre-t-elle ? – **d.** Je préfère le pantalon bleu. – **e.** Il ne veut pas sortir ce soir.

10 « Allô, Louise ? **Où** es-tu ? Nous sommes inquiets. Nous **ne** savons **pas** où tu es. **Qu'est-ce** que tu fais ? **Pourquoi** n'as-tu pas téléphoné ? **Ne** recommence **jamais** ! »

7. Around Pronouns Part 2

1 **a.** Elle **se** réveille à 7 heures tous les matins. – **b.** Je me rappelle de Bruno. – **c.** Nous **nous** sommes encore disputés. – **d.** Vous **vous** téléphonez souvent ? – **e.** Il ne **s'**est pas rasé ce matin.

2 **a.** Elle **se** lève très tôt le mardi matin. – **b.** Je **m'habille** toujours en jean ! – **c.** Il ne **se lave** jamais. Quelle horreur ! – **d.** Nous **nous amusons** beaucoup ! Vive les vacances ! – **e.** Vous **vous couchez** à quelle heure le samedi soir ?

3 **Les montres** = Celles – **L'enfant** = Celui – **La chambre** = Celle – **Les jupes** = Celles – **Le manteau** = Celui – **Les livres** = Ceux

4 **a.** Celui-ci – **b.** Celle-ci – **c.** Ceux-là – **d.** Celui-là – **e.** Ceux-ci.

5 **a.** **Que** fais-tu dans la cuisine ? – **b.** **Qui** a pris mon manteau ? – **c.** **Que** veut-il faire ce soir ? – **d.** **Qui** est ce jeune homme ? – **e.** **Qui** a apporté le gâteau ?

6 « **Quelle** robe veux-tu mettre aujourd'hui ? – Je ne sais pas. Celle qui est jolie. – **Laquelle** ? – La bleue. – Et **quelles** chaussures veux-tu porter ? – Celles qui sont confortables. Mais **lesquelles** ? – Les sandales. Et **quel** chapeau aimerais-tu ? Celui avec une fleur. Merci ! » **[lequel]** n'est pas utilisé.

7 **a.** J'aime **la leur**. – **b.** J'aime **le sien**. – **c.** J'aime **les nôtres**. – **d.** J'aime **la tienne**. – **e.** J'aime **les siennes**.

⑧ **a.** L'enfant **qui** pleurait était perdu. – **b.** Le dernier film **que** j'ai vu était merveilleux. – **c.** La tarte **que** maman a préparée est délicieuse ! – **d.** Je connais la femme **qui** est devant la boutique. – **e.** Je déteste le parfum **que** tu portes aujourd'hui.

⑨ **a.** Le bébé a pleuré toute la nuit, **ce que** j'ai trouvé fatigant. – **b.** Il pleut encore, **ce qui** est très ennuyeux. – **c.** Je t'ai dit de ranger ta chambre, **ce que** je t'ai déjà demandé 3 fois ! – **d.** Le professeur est absent, **ce qui** signifie que nous pouvons rentrer chez nous. – **e.** Il a amené des fleurs, **ce que** je trouve très gentil.

⑩ **a.** As-tu des livres? Oui j'**en** ai. – **b.** Est-il passé au bureau ? Oui, il **y** est allé. – **c.** As-tu acheté des poires ? Non, je n'**en** ai pas acheté. – **d.** Avons-nous des stylos noirs ? Oui, nous **en** avons. – **e.** Jacques était-il au magasin ? Non, il n'**y** était pas.

8. Around Numbers and Time

① 8 = **huit** – 14 = **quatorze** – 21 = **vingt et un** – 50 = **cinquante** – 70 = **soixante-dix** – 76 = **soixante-seize** – 80 = **quatre-vingts** – 90 = **quatre-vingt-dix** – 200 = **deux cents** – 2 000 = **deux mille**.

② 2 + 5 = **sept** – 10 x 8 = **quatre-vingts** – 9 x 2 = **dix-huit** – 10 000 : 10 = **mille** – 51 + 22 = **soixante-treize** – 30 – 9 = **vingt et un** – 35 + 39 = **soixante-quatorze** – 216 : 6 = **trente-six**

③ Number 11 = **onze** is different, it is the only odd number. All others are even numbers!

④ 4e = **quatrième** – 9e = **neuvième** – 16e = **seizième** – 17e = **dix-septième** – 21e = **vingt et unième** – 26e = **vingt-sixième** – 1 000e = **millième**

⑤ **a.** quarantième – **b.** cent vingt-neuvième – **c.** premier – **d.** soixantième – **e.** millième – **f.** trentième.

⑥ Mardi – Jeudi – Samedi – Dimanche.

⑦ Février – Avril – Juin – Août – Octobre – Décembre.

⑧ **a.** I saw Jean-Philippe the day before yesterday. – **b.** What did you do the day after? – **c.** Do you want to go to the cinema next Friday? – **d.** Ella saw this movie last Tuesday. – **e.** The weather is really beautiful today!

⑨ **a.** treize heures quinze / et quart – **b.** seize heures trente – **c.** quatre heures quarante-cinq / cinq heures moins le quart – **d.** vingt heures quarante – **e.** dix heures vingt-cinq.

⑩ Lundi à **neuf heures** M. Dupouy doit se rendre à une réunion qui a lieu au bureau. À **midi et demi** il déjeune avec M. Gosseaume à la Brasserie Dijonnaise puis à **quatorze heures dix** il participe à la présentation du nouveau produit de la compagnie. Le soir même à **dix-huit heures vingt-cinq** il prend l'avion pour Paris.

Le lendemain, M. Dupouy a un rendez-vous avec Dr Garrant à **neuf heures trente**, suivi d'une réunion à La Défense à **onze heures**. Il doit déjeuner à Montmartre à **midi vingt** avec son ami Bastian puis se rend à l'aéroport pour son vol de **quatorze heures quinze**. Il dîne avec sa femme, Marie à **dix-neuf heures**.

Le mercredi, M. Dupouy a un déjeuner avec un collaborateur à **huit heures vingt** puis doit se rendre à une conférence à **treize heures quarante-cinq** à Dijon. À **dix-huit heures**, il doit aller à l'école de son fils pour rencontrer l'instituteur.

⑪ **a.** 90 € – **b.** 6 pièces de 50 cents – **c.** 3 lapins et 2 poules – **d.** 800 minutes (13 heures et 20 minutes).

9. Around the Perfect Tense

① **a.** manger – **b.** boire – **c.** aller – **d.** dormir – **e.** vouloir.

②

	1st Group	2nd Group	3rd group
Chanter	✓		
Punir		✓	
Rendre			✓
Écouter	✓		
Pleuvoir			✓
Grandir		✓	
Devenir			✓
Danser	✓		
Apprendre			✓

③ **a.** détester > détesté – **b.** dîner > dîné – **c.** aimer > aimé – **d.** écouter > écouté – **e.** perdre > perdu – **f.** prendre > pris

④ **a.** Hier, nous avons **appris** une nouvelle leçon ! – **b.** Il m'a **offert** un magnifique bouquet de roses ! – **c.** Elle a **voulu** rentrer tôt à la maison. – **d.** Nous avons **pu** rencontrer le chanteur du groupe. – **e.** Vous avez **fait** vos devoirs ?

⑤ **a.** Elles ont **lu** tous les livres. – **b.** Elles les ont tous **lus**. – **c.** Nous avons **copié** toutes les pages. – **d.** Nous les avons toutes **copiées**. – **e.** Elle n'a pas **pleuré** longtemps.

⑥ **a.** Elle est **allée** en ville avec Sonia. – **b.** Clarèle et moi sommes **rentrés** (moi=masc) / **rentrées** (moi=fem). – **c.** Éléanore et Audrey sont **parties** après le film. – **d.** Alain n'est pas **arrivé**. – **e.** Jean-Luc et Jérôme sont **venus** à 18 heures.

⑦ **a.** Ils se sont encore **disputés** ! – **b.** Elles se sont **échangé** leurs adresses. – **c.** Elle s'est **coupé** le doigt. – **d.** Elles se sont **endormies** devant la télé. – **e.** Ils se sont **regardés** pendant de longues minutes.

⑧ **1.c.** J'ai gagné la course ! – **2.a.** Nous avons vu ta sœur ce matin. – **3.e.** Tu es rentrée à quelle heure ? – **4.f.** Elles sont allées au marché ce matin. – **5.d.** Vous êtes restés au parc toute la journée ? – **6.b.** Ils ont rangé leur chambre.

⑨ **a.** Nous avons **regardé** la télévision toute la nuit ! – **b.** Elles sont **entrées** par la porte de secours. – **c.** J'ai **mis** la voiture dans le garage. – **d.** Tu as **vu** l'éclipse hier soir ? – **e.** Samuel et Laurence ont **écouté** la radio pendant deux heures ! – **f.** Nous avons **pris** un taxi pour rentrer.

⑩ **2.e.** Elles ont téléphoné à l'hôtel pour réserver une chambre. – **3.d.** Elles ont déposé leurs bagages dans la chambre. – **4.f.** Elles ont demandé au concierge l'adresse d'un bon restaurant. – **5.a.** Elles sont restées deux heures au restaurant. – **6.c.** Elles sont rentrées à l'hôtel se coucher.

10. Around the Present Tense

1 **a. Tu** marches vite. – **b. Elles** chantent sous la pluie. – **c.** Il porte des chaussures. – **d. Nous** aidons les sans-abri. – **e. Vous** dansez très bien ! – **f. Je** pense trop !

2 **a.** Les touristes **visitent** le musée. – **b. Tu portes** une jolie jupe. – **c. Nous aimons** la musique classique. – **d.** À quelle heure **arrivez**-vous ? – **e.** Il **chante** très bien.

3 **a.** Je **travaille** dans l'informatique. – **b. Tu visites** ce musée souvent ? – **c.** Il **débute** le travail à 10 heures. – **d. Nous dessinons** ce château régulièrement. – **e.** Vous ne **montez** pas les escaliers ? – **f.** Elles **parlent** trop vite !

4 **a. Nous achetons** des pizzas tous les samedis. – **b.** Qui **appellent**-ils ? – **c.** Il **jette** ses vieilles chaussures. – **d. Vous espérez** encore voir Brad Pitt ! – **e. Nous envoyons** la lettre.

5 **a. Nous commençons** la réunion à 10 heures. – **b.** Je **préfère** le pain complet. – **c. Nous mangeons** au restaurant ce midi. – **d.** Tu te **rappelles** le dernier livre que tu as lu ? – **e.** Elle lui **envoie** une lettre chaque semaine.

6 **a. Tu choisis** d'étudier l'anglais ? – **b. Nous réussissons** toujours les examens d'histoire. – **c.** Elle **maigrit** à vue d'œil ! – **d.** Jacques **punit** souvent son fils. – **e.** Vous ne **réfléchissez** pas assez !

7 **a.** Je **choisis** toujours la mauvaise caisse au supermarché ! – **b. Nous finissons** souvent avant le reste de la classe. – **c. Vous bâtissez** une nouvelle maison ? – **d.** Ils **réussissent** toujours à éviter de faire la vaisselle ! – **e. Tu remplis** trop mon verre !

8 **a. Tu descends** au prochain arrêt ? – **b. Vous perdez** toujours de l'argent au casino ! – **c.** Sophie et Marc **vendent** de très jolies fleurs dans leur magasin. – **d. Nous défendons** souvent notre sœur. – **e.** Ils n'**entendent** pas la cloche de l'église !

9 **a.** Où **mets**-tu les sacs de voyage ? – **b. Savez**-vous à quelle heure part le train ? – **c. Nous voulons** voyager en avion cette fois-ci. – **d. Peux**-tu porter cette valise, s'il te plaît ? – **e. Nous devons** aller au terminal 1 ou au terminal 2 ? – **f.** Je ne **vois** pas notre porte de départ !

10 **a.** Je **me** douche tous les matins. – **b.** Elle **se** brosse les dents deux fois par jour. – **c. Nous nous** lavons les mains constamment. – **d. Vous vous** rongez encore les ongles ! – **e.** Ils **s'habillent** à 7h15 tous les jours.

11 **a. Écoute** le professeur ! – **b.** Ne **regardez** pas par la fenêtre, mais **lisez** votre livre ! – **c. Arrête** de parler avec ton voisin ! – **d. Rendons** nos copies. Le test est terminé. – **e. Prenez** vos livres et **ouvrez**-les à la page 47.

12 **a.** Apprends-le. – **b.** Rangez-les – **c.** Prends-la. – **d.** Éteignons-les – **e.** Accrochez-le.

11. Around the Future Tense

1 **a.** Je **mettrai** mon maillot de bain. – **b. Nous descendrons** au restaurant. – **c.** Le serveur nous **servira** notre cappuccino. – **d. Tu mangeras** une salade de fruits frais. – **e. Nous nous baignerons** dans l'océan turquoise.

2 **a. Nous danserons** toute la nuit ! – **b. Vous choisirez** comme vin, messieurs dames ? – **c. Prendras**-tu de l'eau ? – **d.** Elles **chanteront** longtemps à la soirée karaoké. – **e.** Il **rentrera** tard, c'est sûr !

3 **1.c.** L'**enverras**-tu à Stéphanie ? – **2.b.** Que **ferons**-nous demain ! – **3.a. Viendrez**-vous à nouveau l'année prochaine ? – **4.b. Saurez**-vous retrouver la route ? – **5.c.** Où **irons**-nous après le restaurant ?

4 **a.** [...], je **serai** à la plage ! – **b.** Sandrine, **auras**-tu ton téléphone [...] ? – **c. Vous verrez** ! [...] – **d. Pourrons**-nous faire garder notre petite-fille ? – **e.** Nos filles **iront** en excursion la semaine prochaine !

5 « Marie est très heureuse. Demain, Charles **arrivera** par le train, un bouquet à la main, prêt à l'épouser. Ils **se regarderont** et à cet instant précis, **se reconnaîtront**, pour la vie. [...] Ils **voyageront** autour du monde, **visiteront** tous ces pays dont ils ont parlé sans se lasser. Ils **pourront** parler sans interruption. Qui sait ? Ils **se marieront** ; **auront** des enfants, peut-être. Et **vivront** dans la paix, [...]. Ils **seront** ensemble, unis, contre tous. »

6 **a.** Je **vais** – **b. Tu vas** – **c.** Il/Elle **va** – **d. Nous allons** – **e. Vous allez** – **f.** Ils/Elles **vont**.

7 **a. Nous irons** voir le nouveau film ! – **b. Allez**-vous assister au spectacle ? – **c.** Je ne **vais** pas manger chez Chloé demain midi. – **d.** Il **va** encore manger du chocolat en cachette !– **e.** Quand **vas**-tu aller poster du cartes de Noël ?

8 **a.** Dépêchez-vous ! Le spectacle **va commencer** ! – **b.** Ta voiture est en panne ? Pas de problème ! Je **vais te conduire** au garage. – **c.** Le ciel se couvre : je pense qu'il **va pleuvoir**. – **d.** Les Lagrange **vont visiter** le Vietnam au mois d'août. – **e. Allez-vous partir** en vacances cette année ?

9 **a.** Je **ne vais pas** suivre des cours à l'université l'année prochaine. – **b.** Julie **ne va pas** passer son permis de conduire la semaine prochaine. – **c.** Elles **ne vont pas** se promener en ville cet après-midi. – **d. Vous n'allez pas** rentrer à deux heures ce soir ? – **e. Tu ne vas pas** rester à la maison demain ?

10 **a.** Je **partirai** quand Alexandre **arrivera**. – **b.** Dorian **va aller** chez son frère demain après-midi. – **c.** Élise **sera** déçue lorsqu'elle **apprendra** que Corentin ne vient pas. – **d. Nous viendrons** tous en vacances avec vous l'année prochaine ! – **e.** Que **feras**-tu demain à cette heure-ci ?

12. Around the Past Tense

1 **a.** Nous partons → Je **partais** – **b.** Nous aimons → Ils **aimaient** – **c.** Nous croyons → Tu **croyais** – **d.** Nous prenons → Vous **preniez** – **e.** Nous faisons → Elle **faisait**.

2 **a.** Il **faisait** nuit lorsque l'avion a atterri.– **b. Nous allions** à la plage tous les matins ! – **c. Vouliez**-vous nous voir avant de partir ? – **d.** Je **me sentais** très fatigué. – **e. Vous habitiez** tous ensemble ? Vous **deviez** être à l'étroit ! [cuisinait] n'est pas utilisé.

❸ **a.** Je **savais** que vous **étiez** en France ! – **b.** Il **pensait** que tu **avais** deux chats ! – **c.** Nous **avions** les cheveux blonds quand nous **étions** petits. – **d.** **Mangeais**-tu des pâtes à 3 heures ce matin ? – **e.** Avant, Caroline **appelait** sa sœur tous les soirs.

❹

	Passé composé	Imparfait
a. Je suis allée au théâtre.	✓	
b. Il préparait un gâteau au chocolat.		✓
c. Nous mangions au restaurant.		✓
d. Stéphane a vu un renard dans le pré.	✓	
e. Marie-Luce dormait à poings fermés.		✓
f. Gwendolyne s'est promenée au parc.	✓	
g. Vous avez regardé le film hier soir ?	✓	
h. Je lisais mon livre tranquillement.		✓

❺ **a.** Je **faisais** la sieste lorsque la voisine **a sonné** à la porte. – **b.** Lorsqu'il **est rentré**, Audrey **regardait** la télévision. – **c.** Il **se rendait** à la banque quand il **l'a rencontrée**. – **d.** Elles **étaient** en vacances et elles **ont acheté** de très jolis vêtements. – **e.** Le chat **s'apprêtait** à bondir lorsque l'oiseau **s'est envolé**.

❻ **1.e.** Je visitais l'Italie lorsque j'ai rencontré Lorenzo. – **2.c.** Je garais la voiture quand la Peugeot m'est rentrée dedans ! – **3.f.** Elle plantait de la menthe quand elle s'est fait piquer par une araignée. – **4.b.** Passais-tu ton examen lorsque tu t'es évanouie ? – **5.a.** Il redescendait la montagne quand il est tombé. – **6.d.** Vous faisiez du ski lorsque vous vous êtes rencontrés ?

❼ **a.** Je **partirais** en vacances demain ! – **b.** Julian **finirait** sa toile s'il avait le temps ! – **c.** Avec des « si » on **mettrait** Paris en bouteille ! – **d.** Martine **préférerait** prendre le train. – **e.** Hélène et Simon **vendraient** leur maison !

❽ **a.** Si tu **parlais** moins, tu **finirais** plus vite ! – **b.** Vous vous **amuseriez** vraiment si vous **veniez** en vacances ! – **c.** Si Luc le lui **demandait**, Aline **aimerait** beaucoup l'épouser ! – **d.** Nathan **serait** heureux si Julie lui **écrivait** une lettre.

❾ **a.** Je **verrais** mieux si tu allumais la lumière ! – **b.** Lucas **devrait** arrêter de courir. – **c.** Il **faudrait** un miracle ! – **d.** Il **gagnerait** la course. – **e.** Louise **donnerait** tout ce qu'elle a pour une glace – **f.** Nous **serions** déjà arrivés s'il n'y avait pas tant de circulation.

❿ **a.** Je **préparais** le dîner lorsque Samuel **est arrivé**. – **b.** Si tu **faisais** un effort, tu y **arriverais** ! – **c.** Vous **verriez** la chenille si vous **regardiez** de plus près. – **d.** Nous ne **pourrions** pas comprendre, même si nous **essayions**. – **e.** J'**écoutais** la radio lorsque la nouvelle **est tombée**.

13. Around Prepositions

❶ **a.** Anne et Marie se sont cachées **sous** la table ! – **b.** Vas-tu **chez** tes parents à Pâques ? – **c.** Edwige part **à** Tours avec ses enfants cet après-midi. – **d.** Guy est allé **dans** la forêt cueillir des champignons. – **e.** Elles sont parties **pendant** une heure.

❷ **a.** Nous allons **au** Brésil le mois prochain ! – **b.** Julien voudrait se rendre **en** Inde pour les vacances. – **c.** Nadia vit **aux** Émirats Arabes Unis. – **d.** Pablo est-il né **en** Espagne ou **au** Portugal ? – **e.** J'adorerais passer Noël **aux** Fidji ! – **f.** Kate retourne bientôt **en** Angleterre. – **g.** Tu vas **à** Lille après-demain ?

❸ **a.** Aden vit **à** Marrakech **au** Maroc. – **b.** Acha vit **à** Yaoundé **au** Cameroun. – **c.** Éléonore vit **à** Besançon **en** France. – **d.** Aiko vit **à** Tokyo **au** Japon. – **e.** Eeva vit **à** Helsinki **en** Finlande.

❹ **a.** La balle est tombée **en bas des** escaliers. – **b.** Le poulet est **dans** le frigo. – **c.** Le chat de la voisine est coincé **en haut de** l'arbre ! – **d.** Ton cochon d'Inde se cache encore **sous** le canapé [...] ! – **e.** Pourquoi as-tu garé la voiture **devant** le garage [...] ?

❺ **a.** Le restaurant est-il **loin** de la maison ? [...] – **b.** La boulangerie se trouve **entre** la boucherie et le café. – **c.** Les toilettes sont tout de suite **en haut** des escaliers [...]. – **d.** Je crois que le gâteau est **sur** la table de la cuisine. – **e.** [...] Il y a une énorme araignée **derrière** toi !

❻ **a.** As-tu mis ma chemise **dans** le sac de voyage ? – Oui, elle est **dedans** ! – **b.** Regarde ! Hélène est assise **à côté de** Sébastien ! – **c.** Où est garée ma moto ? – Elle est garée là, **à gauche**. – **d.** Les clés sont **en dessous** de la valise. – **e.** Oh non ! La maison est encore **loin** !

❼ **a.** Je suis arrivé en retard **à l'**école ce matin. – **b.** Vas-tu **à la** fête du village samedi prochain ? – **c.** Ils sont allés **chez** Caroline hier soir. – **d.** Stéphanie a rendez-vous **chez** le médecin vendredi matin à 9h30. – **e.** Elles sont arrivées **aux** urgences vers minuit. – **f.** Il vient d'arriver **au** bureau.

❽ **1.** Je vais : à l'école. – à la pêche avec mon frère ! – au mariage de Maé et Joris. – aux vendanges !
2. Je sors de la boîte de nuit ! – du cours de guitare. – de l'opéra. – du cinéma.

❾ **a.** Nous allons aller à la plage **pendant** les vacances ! – **b.** Le train arrive **dans** une heure ! – **c.** Il habite à Paris **depuis** 2002. – **d.** La famille Charlet déménage **en** septembre. – **e.** Ils parlent **pendant** des heures quand Jonathan téléphone ! – **f.** Il fait beau **depuis** le milieu de l'été.

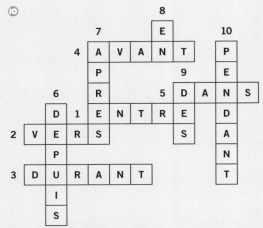

⑪ 1.f. **Au sujet de, à propos de** = about – 2.d. **Avec** = with – 3.c. **Contre** = against – 4.a. **Malgré** = in spite of – 5.h. **Par** = by – 6.b. **Quant à** = as for – 7.i. **Sans** = without – 8.e. **Sauf** = except – 9.g. **Selon** = according to.

⑫ a. Fais attention **aux** trous ! – **b.** Julian joue **de la** guitare. – **c.** Tu commences **à** comprendre cet exercice ! – **d.** J'ai oublié **de** fermer la porte d'entrée ! – **e.** Je me souviens **du** jour où la foudre est tombée sur ta maison !

14. Around Adverbs

❶ a. prudemment – **b.** joliment – **c.** malheureusement – **d.** constamment – **e.** gentiment – **f.** joyeusement – **g.** profondément

❷ a. Luc est tellement fatigué. – **b.** Je ne vais pas souvent au théâtre. – **c.** Il a beaucoup grandi cette année. – **d.** Vous êtes très gentils. – **e.** Il est entré silencieusement dans la maison.

❸ a. C'est le **meilleur** film de l'année ! – **b.** Louis m'a posé la question **gentiment**. – **c.** Est-ce un **bon** dessert ? – **d.** Vous allez **bien** ? – **e.** Karine va beaucoup **mieux** aujourd'hui.

❹ a. Je pars **souvent** en voyage. – **b.** Je travaille **toujours** avec des enfants. – **c.** Je travaille **parfois** avec un ordinateur. – **d.** Je rencontre **souvent** des gens. – **e.** Je bavarde **généralement** avec mes clients.

❺ a. Il n'y va **jamais**. – **b.** Elle n'y va que très **rarement**. – **c.** Nous regardons **toujours** les programmes du soir ensemble ! – **d.** Pas très **souvent,** mais quelquefois il y a un spectacle intéressant. – **e.** Elle en sort **généralement** à 16h30.

❻ a. Nous devons nous lever **tôt**. – **b.** Des nuages sont apparus, **puis** le vent s'est levé. – **c.** Viens **ici** ! – **d.** Ne pleure pas Edwige, ta maman va rentrer **bientôt**. – **e.** J'ai rencontré Carla **il y a** cinq ans et nous ne nous sommes pas quittés depuis ! – **f.** Je viens **souvent** ici. – **g.** J'en cuisine **rarement**.

❼ a. Non, je l'ai cherché **partout** mais ne l'ai trouvé **nulle part**. – **b.** Allez donc jouer **dehors** avec le ballon ! – **c.** J'ai cherché Domino dehors et il était **à l'intérieur** !– **d.** Elle est **là-bas**, à côté des arbres ! Elle était vraiment **loin** ! –

e. Mais, je ne suis pas à l'étage, je suis **en bas** !

❽ a. Il y a **trop** de sucre. – **b.** Il y a **assez** de lait dans mon café. – **c.** Il y avait très **peu de** gens présents. – **d.** Oui, j'aimerais **plus de** sucre dans mon café, s'il vous plaît. – **e.** Il y a **beaucoup de** gâteaux et ils sont tous appétissants !

❾ a. **Où** est Thomas ? – **b. Comment** es-tu allé à Dijon ? – **c. Qui** est avec Florence ? – **d. Quand** venez-vous nous voir ? – **e. Pourquoi** es-tu en colère ?

❿ a. Ma grand-mère conduit si **lentement** !– **b.** Il va **toujours / souvent** au travail en vélo. – **c.** Tu as **probablement** raison. – **d.** Je n'en mange **jamais**. – **e. Malheureusement**, Jennifer et Océane ne pourront pas venir à ton anniversaire. – **f.** Julien est **vraiment** très généreux. – **g.** J'ai **bien** compris.

15. Around Verbs

❶ a. **Devez**-vous aller à l'école demain ? – **b.** Nous ne **pouvons** pas manger ou boire ici. – **c. Puis**-je utiliser les toilettes, s'il vous plaît ? – **d.** Elles **doivent** rentrer à 10 heures. – **e.** Tu **veux** venir avec nous au cinéma ? – **f.** Il **veut** visiter l'Écosse.

❷ a. Camille **peut** venir à la maison cet après-midi ? – **b.** Vous **devez** ôter vos chaussures avant d'entrer. – **c.** Je **dois** étudier pour cet examen ! – **d.** Nous **devons** faire les courses pour le week-end. – **e.** Elles **peuvent** nous entendre !

❸ 1.d. Sortez les skis ! Il neige ! – **2.a.** Je dois trouver mon parapluie ! Il pleut ! – **3.e.** Il faut mettre les manteaux ! Il fait froid ! – **4.b.** Nous pouvons sortir en tee-shirt ! Il fait beau ! – **5.c.** Peux-tu me donner un verre d'eau ? Il fait chaud !

❹ a. Il semble que tu as raison. – **b.** Il fait très beau aujourd'hui ! – **c.** C'est l'été ! Il fait très chaud ! – **d.** Il vaut mieux avoir un portable. – **e.** Il n'y a pas beaucoup de monde / de gens ici.

❺ a. Are you cold? – **b.** I am very hungry. – **c.** We are wrong. – **d.** I am 41. – **e.** You are lucky.

❻ a. Tu as raison ! Il pleut ! – **b.** J'ai vraiment froid ! Ferme la fenêtre ! – **c.** Nous avons de la chance ! Nous avons gagné / On a gagné ! – **d.** Quel âge a-t-elle ? – Elle a 26 ans. – **e.** As-tu faim ?

❼

Sentence	T	I
a. Nous mangeons une pizza tous les vendredis.	✓	
b. Sabine écoute une chanson.	✓	
c. Corinne parle à ses amis.		✓
d. Tu réponds à tante Colette ?		✓
e. Je bois du café tous les matins.	✓	

❽

Sentence	D	I
a. J'ai donné mon livre.	✓	
b. Elle téléphone à Alice.		✓

c. Nous écrivons à nos parents.		✓
d. Tu chantes cette chanson.	✓	
e. Nous pensons à nos vacances.		✓

5 **a.** lançant – **b.** aimant – **c.** achetant – **d.** voyant – **e.** maigrissant – **f.** venant – **g.** s'habillant.

16. Around Linking Words

1 **a.** Je suis passé chez toi, <u>mais</u> tu n'étais pas là. – **b.** <u>Soit</u> tu viens avec nous, <u>soit</u> tu ne viens pas […] – **c.** Marion pense cuisiner un bœuf bourguignon <u>ou</u> un navarin. – **d.** La voiture est au garage <u>donc</u> je ne pourrai pas venir te voir ce matin. – **e.** Je ne me sens pas très bien, <u>cependant</u> j'essaierai d'aller en cours.

2 **a.** Julien se pose des questions **à savoir** si la maison sera vendue. – **b.** Laetitia n'aime pas skier, **c'est pourquoi** elle reste au chalet. – **c.** Florian ne s'énerve jamais, **au contraire** il reste toujours serein. – **d.** Marine n'aime pas le chocolat, **pourtant** elle a fait […]. – **e.** Maxime lui fait confiance, **cependant** il a un doute. – **f.** Je suis au lit **car** je suis malade.

3 **a.** Claudette a pris un parapluie <u>au cas où</u> il pleuve. – **b.** <u>Bien que</u> Pierre ait peur de l'eau, ils sont allés en vacances au bord de la mer. – **c.** <u>Comme</u> les enfants n'aiment pas la télévision, j'ai apporté <u>des</u> jeux de société. – **d.** Je partirai <u>lorsque</u> le film sera fini. – **e.** <u>Depuis que</u> j'ai 18 ans, je me <u>sens</u> beaucoup plus libre !

4 **a.** Aussitôt que = Dès que – **b.** Comme = Puisque – **c.** Lorsque = Quand – **d.** Bien que = Quoique.

5 **a.** Depuis que je **suis** en retraite, […] ! – **b.** Si tu **vas** en ville demain, préviens-moi ! – **c.** Bien que les chiens me **fassent** peur, […]! – **d.** Quand tu **arriveras**, […]. – **e.** Quoi que nous **disions**, […].

6 **Premièrement / D'abord / Tout d'abord** = firstly – **En premier lieu** = in the first place – **Deuxièmement** = secondly – **Ensuite / Puis** = then

7 **D'un côté... de l'autre** = on the one hand… on the other… – **D'une part... d'autre part...** = on the one hand… on the other… – **Ou... Ou...** = either… or… – **Par ailleurs** = in addition – **En outre** = moreover

D'un autre côté = on the other hand – **Par contre** = on the other hand – **En revanche** = on another hand – **Au contraire** = on the contrary

8 **Ainsi** = in this way – **Par exemple** = for example – **Notamment** = particularly – **En particulier** = in particular

9 **Finalement / Enfin** = finally – **En conclusion / pour conclure** = to conlude – **En résumé** = to summarize / to sum up – **En bref** = in short – **Pour finir** = finally

10 **a.** **D'un côté**, tu pourrais penser […], mais **de l'autre** […]. – **b.** Je n'aime pas certains gâteaux : **par exemple**, le mille-feuille […]. – **c.** **Premièrement**, j'aimerais présenter […]. – **d.** **D'abord** on travaille ; **ensuite** on s'amuse ! – **e.** Elle a pris son parapluie ; elle sera **ainsi** protégée de la pluie.

17. Around the Passive

1

	Active	Passive
a. La vaisselle est faite par Joël.		✓
b. Catherine range le garage.	✓	
c. Le chat est brossé par Manon.		✓
d. Cette lettre est écrite par mon arrière-grand-mère !		✓
e. Mon père a peint cette toile.	✓	

2 **a.** Notre maison **est** construite […]. – **b.** Les haricots **sont** plantés par Julien. – **c.** Nous **sommes** accueillis […]. – **d.** Vous **êtes** poursuivis […] ! – **e.** Tu **es** invitée par Ella !

3 **a.** Ces tartes **sont préparées** […] – **b.** L'arbre de Noël **est décoré** par les enfants. – **c.** Le président français **est accueilli** par le premier ministre anglais. – **d.** Les voleurs **sont arrêtés** par la police. – **e.** Les commandes **sont prises** par la serveuse.

4 **a.** Cette sculpture **a été réalisée** […]. – **b.** Ce livre **a été écrit** […]. – **c.** La voiture **a été vendue** […]. – **d.** Ces crevettes **ont été préparées** […]. – **e.** Le ciel **a été illuminé** […].

5 **a.** **On a réparé** le bateau. – **b.** **On a changé** le numéro. – **c.** **On a ouvert** le magasin. – **d.** **On a cassé** le vase. – **e.** **On a bâti** la maison.

6 **a.** Comment cela **se dit**-il en anglais ? – **b.** Le vin blanc **se sert** très frais. – **c.** Cela ne **se fait** pas. Ce n'est pas poli. – **d.** Ce plat **se mange** chaud et accompagné de haricots blancs. – **e.** Les toilettes **se trouvent** au fond du couloir.

7 **a.** Une pomme **a été mangée par** Caroline – **b.** La Joconde **a été peinte par** Léonard de Vinci. – **c.** Le ver de terre **a été mangé par** l'oiseau. – **d.** Les jonquilles **ont été plantées par** Daniel. – **e.** L'appartement **a été décoré par** Mathilde.

8

	Active	Passive
Les cambrioleurs ont été surpris par les policiers.		✓
Notre président était respecté de tous.		✓
On interdit l'utilisation des téléphones portables dans la salle d'attente.	✓	
Ce fruit ne se mange pas.	✓	
Karine est très appréciée de ses collègues.		✓

9

Verb	Yes	No
Demander quelque chose à quelqu'un		✓
Construire quelque chose pour quelqu'un	✓	
Aller quelque part		✓
Admirer par quelqu'un	✓	
Promettre quelque chose à quelqu'un		✓
Monter les escaliers		✓

| **Manger** quelque chose | ✓ | |
| **Tomber** par terre | | ✓ |

18. Around the Present of the Subjunctive

❶ a. Il faut que je **réussisse** [...]. – **b.** [...] avant que Jean **vienne** me chercher. – **c.** Pourvu que nous **vendions** [...]. – **d.** [...] que tu **agrandisses** [...] ! – **e.** [...] que tu **prennes** [...].

❷ a. [...] que je **mange** [...]. – **b.** [...] que tu **écoutes** la radio. – **c.** [...] qu'elle **maigrisse** très vite. – **d.** [...] que nous **mettions** la table. – **e.** [...] que vous **perdiez** [...]. – **f.** [...] qu'ils **choisissent** toujours les bonnes cartes.

❸ a. [...] que tu **sois** [...]. – **b.** [...] que nous **soyons** [...]. – **c.** que vous **soyez** à l'heure. – **d.** [...] que je **sois** [...]. – **e.** [...] qu'elle **soit** [...]. – **f.** Bien qu'ils **soient** [...].

❹ a. Bien que je n'**aie** [...]. – **b.** Il faut que tu **aies** [...]. – **c.** [...] qu'elle **ait** [...]. – **d.** [...] qu'ils **aient** [...]. – **e.** [...] que vous **ayez** [...]. – **f.** [...] que nous **ayons** [...].

❺ a. [...] que vous **veniez** [...]. – **b.** [...] que tu **saches** [...]. – **c.** [...] que tu **fasses** [...]. – **d.** [...] que vous **deviez** [...]. – **e.** [...] que ton père **prenne** [...]. – **f.** [...] que tu **ailles** [...].

❻ a. [...] que vous **buviez** [...] ! – **b.** [...] qu'ils **aillent** [...]. – **c.** [...] que tu **reçoives** [...]. – **d.** [...] que tu **tiennes** [...]. – **e.** [...] que vous **fassiez** [...].

❼ a. Je viendrai samedi, **à moins que** [...]. – **b.** J'ai apporté cette couverture **pour que** [...]. – **c. Bien que** je n'aime pas [...]. – **d. Pourvu qu'**il ne vienne pas [...]. – **e.** Je continuerai les leçons **jusqu'à ce que** [...].

❽ a. [...] que nous **gagnions** [...]. – **b.** [...] que tu **viennes** [...]. – **c.** [...] que vous **finissiez** [...]. – **d.** [...] que tu **veuilles** [...]. – **e.** [...] que vous **ayez** [...].

❾ a. Il est impossible que j'aie perdu [...]. – **b. Il est probable qu'**il y ait [...]. – **c. Il est possible que** nous soyons sélectionnés [...]. – **d. Il est possible que** ma jambe soit cassée. – **e. Il est douteux que** j'aie la rubéole.

❿ a. Il serait étonnant que je **reçoive** [...]. – **b.** C'est dommage que tu ne **boives** pas de cidre. – **c.** Il vaut mieux que nous **allions** au cinéma [...]. – **d.** Il est bizarre que tu **aies** un chien [...]. – **e.** Il faut que nous **rendions** nos livres [...].

⓫ a. C'est le meilleur film que j'**aie** jamais vu ! – **b.** Où que tu ailles [...]. – **c. Quoi que** tu fasses [...]. – **d.** Je ne crois pas qu'il **soit** [...]. – **e.** Je ne pense pas qu'il **mange** de viande.

19. Around The Past Historic

❶ Il était une fois un meunier qui, lorsqu'il **mourut**, **légua** tous ses biens à ses trois fils. L'aîné **hérita** d'un moulin, le cadet d'un âne, et le plus jeune, Paul, d'un chat. « Lorsque je l'aurai mangé, **soupira**-t-il, il ne me restera plus qu'à mourir de faim ! » Mais le chat l'**entendit** et **prépara** un plan : [...] Paul était sceptique, mais **fit** ce que le chat lui demandait : « Aussi, si quelqu'un vous le demande, vous vous appelez désormais monsieur le Marquis de Carabas », **ajouta** le chat. Le chat **mit** de la nourriture dans son sac et **s'allongea** sur le sol, comme mort.

❷ a. La réunion **débuta** à 10 heures. – **b.** Clément et Zoé **arrivèrent** à l'aéroport à l'heure. – **c.** Nous **attendîmes** pendant des heures. La tension **monta**. – **d.** Vous **partîtes**. La maison **sembla** vide. – **e.** Je **pris** beaucoup de photos.

❸ a. Elles **eurent** soudain très soif. – **b.** Nous **eûmes** l'idée d'aller au cinéma tous ensemble. – **c.** Lorsqu'elle ouvrit la fenêtre, j'**eus** très froid. – **d.** Il **eut** une peur bleue lorsque la foudre tomba sur la maison voisine ! – **e.** Vous **eûtes** beaucoup de difficultés à organiser ce voyage.

❹ a. Ils **furent** les premiers soldats américains à Paris – **b.** Nous **fûmes** très surpris. – **c.** Louis de Funès **fut** très célèbre dans les années 1970 – **d.** Tu **fus** un des élèves les plus populaires du lycée. – **e.** Vous **fûtes** très heureux de réussir votre examen.

❺ Le Petit Poucet **dut** se lever de bon matin et **prit** le chemin du ruisseau. Il emplit ses poches de petits cailloux blancs et **revint** ensuite à la maison. Il **alla** dans une forêt dense. Le bûcheron **se mit** à couper du bois et les enfants ramassèrent des brindilles. Lorsque les parents **virent** que les enfants étaient occupés, ils s'enfuirent rapidement. Le Petit Poucet **courut** partout pour retrouver ses parents mais **dut** renoncer, tristement.

❻ a. Elle **mit** sa robe rapidement pour ne pas être en retard. – **b.** Ils **reconnurent** le bandit et lui **coururent** après. – **c.** Je **sus** immédiatement que quelque chose lui était arrivé. – **d.** Nous **allâmes** au restaurant après la cérémonie. – **e.** Vous **dûtes** prendre le train plus tard que prévu suite aux intempéries;

❼ a. Ils **avancèrent** dans la neige avec difficulté. – **b.** Nous **voyageâmes** pendant deux mois ! – **c.** Il **neigea** toute la journée. – **d.** Vous **commençâtes** la réunion sans Romain. – **e.** Martin **remplaça** David qui était malade. – **f.** Vous **nageâtes** pendant deux heures !

❽

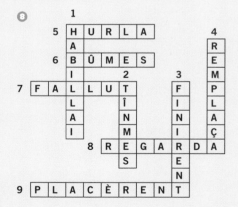

❾ Il était une fois une petite poule rousse qui **sortit** de chez elle pour aller en ville. Elle **mit** la clé dans sa poche mais sa poche avait un trou et la clé **tomba** par terre. La petite poule ne le **vit** pas et **poursuivit** son chemin.
Maître Renard apparut. Il n'avait qu'une envie : manger la poulette ! Lorsqu'il **aperçut** la clé sur le sol, il la **ramassa** et **couru** ouvrir la porte de la maisonnette.

20. Revision Games

1 **a.** J'ai **le** cafard – **b.** Tu me casses **les** oreilles ! – **c.** Il m'a posé **un** lapin ! – **d.** C'est la fin **des** haricots ! – **e.** Arrête de faire **l'**andouille !

2 **a.** un **professeur** = a teacher / lecturer / professor – **b.** un **chanteur** = a singer – **c.** une **vendeuse** = a shop assistant (female) – **d.** un **médecin** = a doctor – **e.** un **ingénieur** = an engineer – **f.** un **serveur** = a waiter – **g.** un **concierge** = a caretaker – **h.** un **boulanger** = a baker

3 **a. est** = être (others: avoir) – **b. étant** = present participle (others: past participles) – **c. te** = direct object pronoun (others: personal subject pronouns) – **d. Mexique** = country (others = nationalities) – **e. chat** = animal (others = colours)

4

(crossword grid)

VRAIES
GENTIL
BONNE
PATIENT
GRAND VIEUX
SÛR
MECHANT

5 **a.** Quentin est allé au cinéma avec ses amis. – **b.** Je pense faire un grand voyage l'année prochaine. – **c.** Ils organiseront une fête d'anniversaire pour Marion. – **d.** Je faisais la sieste lorsque tu as frappé à la porte. – **e.** Eva commencera le travail dès son retour.

6

	Present	Perfect
Regarder	Je regarde	**J'ai regardé**
Faire	**Tu fais**	**Tu as fait**
Vendre	Il vend	**Il a vendu**
Finir	**Nous finissons**	Nous avons fini
Boire	**Vous buvez**	**Vous avez bu**
Aller	Elles vont	**Elles sont allées**

Future	Conditional	Imperfect
Je regarderai	**Je regarderais**	**Je regardais**
Tu feras	**Tu ferais**	Tu faisais
Il vendra	Il vendrait	**Il vendrait**
Nous finirons	**Nous finirions**	**Nous finissions**
Vous boirez	Vous boiriez	Vous buviez
Elles iront	Elles iraient	**Elles allaient**

7 `01:30` = Il est une heure trente.

`04:30` = Il est quatre heures et demie.

`10:45` = Il est onze heures moins le quart.

`02:15` = Il est deux heures et quart.

`12:00` = Il est midi.

`07:50` = Il est huit heures moins dix.

`03:25` = Il est trois heures vingt-cinq.

8

	A	C	O	M	M	E	P
	I				L	O	
	N				O	U	
Q	S	C		R	R		
U	I		A	S	T		
Q	O	D		R	Q	A	
U	I	O		O	U	N	
A		Q	N	E	T		
M	N		U		C		
A	D		E				
I	T	O	U	T	E	F	O	I	S
S			A	U	S	S	I
N	E	A	N	M	O	I	N	S

9 **a.** J'ai rêvé que je gagnais au loto ! – **b.** Il a été au cinéma hier. – **c.** Vous avez aimé ma tarte aux pommes ? – **d.** Tu as compris l'exercice de grammaire ? – **e.** Nous sommes partis à 8 heures.

10 **a.** 46 = quarante-six – **b.** 99 = quatre-vingt-dix-neuf – **c.** 318 = trois cent dix-huit – **d.** 72 = soixante-douze – **e.** 502 = cinq cent deux – **f.** 152 = cent cinquante-deux – **g.** 1008 = mille huit – **h.** 683 = six cent quatre-vingt-trois

Congratulations! You have completed this workbook! It is now time to assess your skills and to add up all the icons for the final assessment. Write the results of each chapter in the boxes below and add them up so as to obtain the final number of icons in each coloured category. Time to find out your results!

	🙂	😐	🙁		🙂	😐	🙁
1. Alphabet and Pronunciation				11. Around the Future Tense			
2. Around Articles & Nouns				12. Around the Past Tense			
3. Around Pronouns Part 1				13. Around Prepositions			
4. Around Adjectives				14. Around Adverbs			
5. Around Comparatives and Superlatives				15. Around Verbs			
6. Around Sentence and Forms				16. Around Linking Words			
7. Around Pronouns Part 2				17. Around the Passive			
8. Around Numbers and Time				18. Around the Present of the Subjunctive			
9. Around the Perfect Tense				19. The Past Historic Tense			
10. Around the Present Tense				20. Revision Games			

Total all chapters .... 🙂 😐 🙁

You mostly have...

🙂

Bravo ! You now master the basics of the French language and are now ready to move up to level 3!

😐

Pas mal du tout ! But there is still room for improvement! Do the exercises that you found difficult again and read the lessons one more time!

🙁

Encore un petit effort ! You are a bit rusty... Read the whole workbook again until you fully understand the lessons and do the exercises again until you get the answers right! Bonne chance !

© 2015 Assimil
Dépôt légal : juillet 2015
N° d'édition : 3452
ISBN : 978-2-7005-0711-9
www.assimil.com
Imprimé en Slovénie par DZS

Conception graphique : MediaSarbacane
Mise en pages : Aurélia Monnier pour Céladon éditions
Réalisation : Céladon éditions, www.celadoneditions.com